4/30/00

Dear Sarah & Chris,

My friends + the
wonderful parents
of my "God children".

Love you,

Margaret Smith

Both Sides of the Rainbow

Both Sides of the Rainbow

BY

TOM CHRISTOPHER AND MARGIE K. CARROLL

ARCANGELA PRESS, INC.

Library of Congress Card Number: 99-66054
ISBN: 0-9674998-0-1

Arcangela Press, Inc.
Suite 240 #A
3605 Sandy Plains Road
Marietta, GA 30066
http://www.bothsidesoftherainbow.com

For Earl, Gloria, Iggy, Bill, Jim, and Charlotte

Acknowledgments

Our heartfelt thanks go out to Carmen Acevedo Butcher whose expertise in editing and dedication to perfection expedited the completion of *Both Sides of the Rainbow*. Along with Carmen several others contributed in helping us with the tedious editing tasks. D. A., Louise, Felicia, Joy, and Esther, we appreciate your time and piercing eyes that burned holes in our manuscript and helped us in the creative process. Your encouragement and knowledge has been invaluable. Thank you, friends.

CONTENTS

1. Manuscript   15
2. Birth   23
3. Wee-Wee   27
4. Mrs. Ball   29
5. Bugs   33
6. Potatohead   37
7. Turd   39
8. Arcangela   43
9. Dance   47
10. Fire Drill   49
11. Runaway   51
12. Sherry   57
13. Jacket   61
14. Devonshire   67
15. Mascot   69
16. Barry   73
17. Funeral   75
18. Weddings   81
19. Benny   85
20. Lucille   89
21. Train   93

22. Meeting   95
23. Model   99
24. California   103
25. Bette   107
26. Francesca   111
27. Rock   115
28. Tree   119
29. Chandelier   125
30. Duck   129
31. Move out   133
32. Babs   137
33. Hattie   141
34. Penthouse   145
35. Friends   149
36. Pussy Soufflé   155
37. Girls   159
38. Rescue   165
39. Cinco De Mayo   169
40. Lana   175
41. Snake   179
42. Scraps   183
43. Bedford   185
44. Titties   189
45. Rich   193
46. Aerobics   199
47. Choir   203
48. Homeless   207
49. Vacations   209

50. Liz   215
51. Jules   219
52. Greg   225
53. Drowning Boy   229
54. Celebrations   233
55. Marilyn   237
56. Cocaine   239
57. Effie's   241
58. Crash   243
59. Oscars   249
60. Grace   253
61. Davis   259
62. Rolls   263
63. Blue Cheese   271
64. Lucy   275
65. Wallace   279
66. Mae   283
67. Garbo   289
68. Frank   293
69. J.C.   295
70. Von   299
71. Destruction   305
72. It's Over   309
73. Ring   313

"Some people survive the Hollywood fast lane
with drugs and booze,
others with divorces,
multiple marriages, even suicide.
I survived by leaving."
-TONY SOMERTINO

1

MANUSCRIPT

MATTHEW SMILED INTO HIS PILLOW AS HE HEARD THE DOWNSTAIRS clock chime six and begin "Edelweiss." His lover, Eric, lay asleep next to him with Cody curved under his arm and Cali was warm against his own body, one curious eye watching him watch Eric. This was his family now—Eric and their West Highland terriers, Cali and Cody.

"Thank you for my blessings, God," Matthew continued his prayers, "Thank you for giving me my soul mate and two precious puppies."

Eric breathed rhythmically, his hand caressing Cody who twitched a bit. "Probably chasing dream squirrels again," Matthew thought with a grin. He had never hoped to have such peacefulness in his lifetime.

Cody shifted and Eric gathered him closer; his Bulgari emerald and gold ring looked stunning against Cody's white coat. Matthew's fingers tightened around the heavy gold band Eric had given him in return. "Just proves that dreams can change," he thought.

A muffled alarm sounded the start of another day. Eric untangled himself from Cody and hit the top of the clock.

"Good morning, Matthew. Did you sleep well?"

"Yeah, and you?"

"The best," Eric said, with a certain mysterious tone.

For a while they lay still and quiet.

"Eric? What do you mean, 'The best'?"

"I had a dream. I can't remember it all. Something big happened to us. Money, travel, celebrity. Matthew, I swear, it seemed so real. It was some ride."

"Try to remember."

"Can't. We did something remarkable, crazy as that sounds. The press was setting up flood lights on our lawn and we were excited because Diane Sawyer was coming to interview us for 'Prime Time.'"

"Come on, think. What did we do?"

Eric arched his back, forcing Cody to relocate. He ran his hand through his curly hair. "I have no idea, Matthew."

"Great, the most fabulous event of our lives, possibly lost forever. Did we live here in Georgia? Were we living on Oakwood? Did Peggy, Kay, and Charlotte live across the street? Can't you remember?"

Eric closed his eyes and lay still a bit longer. "I was driving home from work. I turned onto Oakwood Drive and saw a huge commotion on our street. People were standing around in small groups and a truck with a satellite dish on top was parked near our front walk. Yes, our friends were there, even Sara. We waved as I pulled into the driveway."

"You weren't scared?"

"No. We were expecting it. I can't remember why they wanted to interview us."

"Eric, I believe we are given signs about things. Now, think, Crazy."

"I'll think about it today. Maybe it'll come back to me. It was terribly exciting."

Matthew smiled at Eric, "He's holding out on me," he thought as he got out of bed and padded downstairs with Cody and Cali following. Their new collars jingled slightly as they shook off the night's deep sleep. He moved toward the kitchen door, taking careful steps to avoid the eager, circling dogs. Sometimes dog duty was Eric's chore, if you could call it that. Today Eric would be working at his Buckhead office and barely had time to shower and to eat a bite before tackling the Atlanta rush hour traffic.

Cody and Cali scrambled out the door at full tilt, their ears plastered back, their blurry feet racing them about the yard. The sun peeked over the new backyard fence and cast a soft glow across Matthew's olive-skinned face. He had a certain feeling that Eric's dream was auspicious, and he smiled a knowing smile.

Eric noticed everything from the upstairs bedroom window—Matthew's thick black hair, his smile, and Cody and Cali. He tapped on the window and all three turned toward the sound. Matthew waved, but the terriers had found something much more interesting, a squirrel in an oak tree.

"Hush, Cody, you'll wake the neighbors. Come on, boys, time for breakfast."

Matthew fed them and then prepared a quick breakfast for Eric. He contemplated their good fortune as he set the table. They had moved to Georgia from Florida shortly after meeting and even though Eric had changed employers, his profession as a book agent was providing them with a comfortable living. Eric had brought with him several loyal clients from his previous agency and did put in extra hours with his new company, the Martindorf Literary Agency. Queries and manuscripts were sent to his home offfice as well as the main office in Atlanta where he worked four days a week..

Matthew poured the orange juice and they grabbed a quick bite. There was not much time for talk, but they would call throughout the day and catch up on any news. Eric rose to leave, then turned to bound back up the stairs for his briefcase. Matthew yelled, "Oh, I almost forgot. Three manuscripts came in the mail yesterday."

"Really?" Eric called down. "Where are they? I'll look over them today, but only if I have time."

"Two seemed horrible. You can skim them later, but one looked promising. In fact, I think you're going to like it."

"Okay," Eric puffed as he swept through the kitchen on his way out the door.

Matthew popped the thick manuscript into Eric's briefcase and waved to him as he ran out to the garage. "Call me."

"Okay."

Eric couldn't resist lowering the top of his silver BMW convertible for the 20-minute ride to his office. He sat his coffee cup in its holder, waved goodbye to Cody and Cali, and honked at Matthew as he backed out of the driveway. Matthew saw him wave his cellular phone high in the air.

"I give him 15 minutes before he calls," he thought.

As soon as Eric exited the expressway and headed down West Paces Ferry Road, he grabbed the phone and called Matthew. While he waited for Matthew to answer, he drank in the beauty of the mansion-lined street that was a showplace of blooming azaleas, dogwoods, and gardenias. The manicured grounds were alive with the bright bulbs of spring. April in Atlanta, what a well-kept secret, he thought.

"Hello."

"Hi,"

"Where are you?"

"About a mile from the Governor's mansion and the flowers are magnificent."

"Yes, well, and what about our flowers and garden?"

"Almost as beautiful as that. Still we need to get the boys and ride back down here for you to enjoy this for yourself."

"Okay, Eric. Gotta go. I told Cara I'd pick her up to go to the store. Need to get lettuce and French bread."

"What about chicken breasts? I thought you were going to grill out tonight."

"What? What do you know? I marinated some last night in the refrigerator, Crazy."

"Crazy. Okay, sounds great. I'm almost at the office. Gotta go."

"Bye. "

Eric parked and dashed up the three brick steps into the renovated two-story home of the Martindorf Literary Agency. He breezed past the secretary, Ms. Collins, with a cheery smile and warm, "Good morning, Kathy. How are you?"

"Fine, sir. Did you enjoy the weekend? Get any rest?"

"Yes, yes, I did. Any particular reason you're asking?"

Ms. Collins' eyes darted to a four-foot-high manuscript stack teetering next to her desk. "Remember, Phillip is gone to the Miami Literary Conference till Thursday. It's just you and me, babe."

"Oh, I forgot. Any calls?"

"Does a bear-"

"Don't finish that."

Kathy handed Eric a small stack of pink message slips and pointed him toward the fresh pot of coffee and a box of fresh Krispy Kreme donuts. He poured a cup and backed into his office.

"Hold any call unless it's Phillip or Matthew, okay?"

Eric crossed the room and tipped the blinds to reveal the magnificent morning. He inhaled the coffee aroma and glanced around his renovated office. The hunter green walls had a calming effect on him and the new leather chairs facing his mahogany desk set the perfect tone for a successful book agent. He leaned back with the phone messages and began calling agents, writers, and clients.

Before coming on board with the prestigious Martindorf Literary Agency, Eric had worked for the Hilliard Corporation in Florida where it had sucked the life's blood out of its agents. Before he left, however, he had ferreted out several promising writers and had been instrumental in giving them a start in the world of publishing. He was proud of that.

Two years ago he had heard of the Martindorf tragedy. Phillip Martindorf's son and partner, Halland, had died in a fiery car crash. Through the business grapevine, Eric discovered that Mr. Martindorf was looking for another agent who could fill his son's shoes. After all, the agency was booming, Phillip was only 59, and he thought he had nothing else to live for. After several interviews, Eric had been hired.

No regrets, he thought as he focused on the projects for the day. He unlatched the worn brass latches on his scuffed leather briefcase and saw the expandable file folder tied with a string. Matthew had aroused his curiosity. Better skim this first, he thought. When would people learn? It is improper to send an entire manuscript to an agent. All I want is an overview, a query letter, and three chapters of their books. He was further disgusted to find that there was no SASE enclosed to return the manuscript. Still, Matthew had liked the manuscript. So he opened the thick folder and pulled out a short introductory letter.

January 20, 2000

Dear Mr. Eric Trainer:

Enclosed please find a manuscript I've written that will interest many readers.

First, let me say that this is the true story of my life. I'm quite certain you will find it entertaining, earthy, and, at times, shocking as I lived in Beverly Hills for 24 years and was privileged to count many celebrities as friends and acquaintances. My lover for that almost quarter-of-a-century was a handsome movie star who was married to one of the world's most beautiful women.

In preparing this manuscript, I tape-recorded events in my life, then wrote them as short vignettes. The result is a compilation of my adventures as a young Catholic boy, a model, and later the companion of the brilliant star, Brik Moor III. Along the way I discover some of life's mysteries, many of life's joys, and the importance of being true to one's self.

Some of the names have been changed to protect the privacy of those mentioned because it is not my intention to demean or embarrass anyone. I just want to share my life with others.

The title, *Both Sides of the Rainbow*, exactly describes it. I had the Rolls-Royce, the mansions, and limitless access to money, but I have found true happiness in a relationship lived out in a much less grand style, with a true, deep love whom I was searching for all along. I wrote this book to honor my family and friends. Without their guidance, love, and support, my life would have been less meaningful and certainly less colorful.

Mr. Trainer, the format of this book is unusual. I am less a writer and more a raconteur—a reporter of a wild roller coaster ride. Strap in, and enjoy the view from *Both Sides of the Rainbow*.

Sincerely,

Tony Somertino

Well, this could be interesting Eric thought as he turned to the first story.

2

BIRTH

MY MOM, PALMA, AND DAD, FRANK, MET DURING WORLD WAR II.
Mother was 12 years younger than Dad and came from a
northern Italian family. Her family was blond, blue-eyed, and
slender (the way many people want to look). In stark contrast,
my dad was from the southern tip of Sicily and was dark, chubby,
but very loving.

When they began their courtship, both sets of parents
objected. My dad's Sicilian mother said to him, "Couldn't you
find a girl without French blood in her? She's a whore. She'll
be running around on you everywhere you turn."

My northern Italian grandfather wanted to know "why...[my
mother]...couldn't find a white boy to marry." Their marriage
proved that opposites do attract.

I was both trouble and delight from the beginning. I was
born on the 4th of July, 1950, at 7:00 p.m. As luck would have
it, my mother went into labor just as the entire pediatric ward
made their plans to leave the hospital to join their families for
the 4th of July celebrations. My imminent arrival caused the
delivery staff to postpone their plans and hang around until I
was born.

St. Mary's Hospital in Passaic, New Jersey, overlooked a public park where patriots of all ages were gathered to celebrate victory over the British some 200 years before. From my mom's window, Dad could see the barbecue pits being fired up, children twirling hula hoops, and a general chaos of dogs playing tag with old acquaintances...that is, until the firecrackers came out. Dad stood looking out the window and gave Mom a moment-by-moment commentary of the goings-on in the park. He was also wishing he could participate in the fun playing out below him. He closed his eyes and imagined picnicking with his beautiful two-year-old daughter, Francesca, and his lovely wife.

As 7:00 o'clock approached, the intensity of the partying increased with popping firecrackers, sparklers, and bottle rockets rising high over the canopy of elm trees that ringed the playground. Mom became the center of attention because everyone wanted to leave. They kept passing by her room and glaring at her, willing her to get it over with. The nurses' and doctors' families ran in from the festivities to see when they could come out and join the fun. Dad was ushered out of Mom's room as her labor intensified; he was relegated to the waiting room.

Finally, at exactly 7:00 p.m., I was born. Patriotic music filled the room from the pavilion below, where the Passaic High School marching band was performing its well-rehearsed repertoire. The light from bursting bottle rockets and exploding fireworks lit up the room. While the delivery staff gave cries of appreciation for the amazing fireworks, Mom remembers it felt as if the hospital were under siege as the room crackled with blasts of sparkling, flashing colors.

I was by no means the center of attention. The doctors and nurses worked mechanically, delivering me as quickly as they could because they most wanted their freedom. I was dangled upside down between the doctor's slippery fingers, slapped, mopped up a bit, and flopped down onto my relieved mom.

"It's a girl," the doctor announced.

"Welcome, little Mary Elizabeth," Mom whispered.

In their haste, the doctors had mis-sexed me. Mother curled me in her arms, gently lifted the cotton blanket, and checked me over. First, she cupped my tiny fingers in hers and wondered at their perfection. Next, she slid her warm hands to my legs and counted my toes. Her examination continued to the protruding, swollen navel where the umbilical cord had been perfectly tied off. Still, she almost missed it. My penis that is.

"Why, Miss Mary Elizabeth, we'd better call you Antonio Alberto Somertino," she whispered in my ear. The stirring rendition of the "Star Spangled Banner" filled the room as Mom's heart swelled with pride. A son, she thought, a wonderful son. God had blessed her with her own little 4th of July firecracker.

"Honey," Mom whispered to my dad who had been ushered in to be at her side. He crossed the room and kissed my mom and me. "Meet your son, Antonio."

3

WEE-WEE

MY POOR SISTER, FRANCESCA, WAS A PERFECT DREAM OF A CHILD to raise because she tended to be quiet and complacent. She was the type of kid you could place in a chair and she would stay there for ten years. My hyperactivity, on the other hand, even confounded my maternal grandmother. Once when she saw Mom, Francesca, and me coming up her walk, she pretended she wasn't home. One of the kinder things you could say about me as a child was that I wasn't dull. Neither was our family life. For some reason, I always seemed to be on a mission. My little brain would concoct a farfetched idea, and I would pursue it with a robot-like intensity. For instance, my baby bed was reinforced with extension bars to keep me from making nightly escapes to Mrs. Ball's apartment across the hall. Ha! Good luck.

Even though I was only two years of age, I would somehow rattle my way out of the cage, drag a stool to the door, unlock it, grab Mrs. Ball's key off a hook on the wall, and let myself into her apartment. In the dark I'd toddle down her hall and crawl into bed with her. I just adored Mrs. Ball. She would get up, jot down my whereabouts on a note, and leave it on our apartment door for my poor mom to find the next morning. I always had wonderful dreams when I was nestled in her arms.

Once, while a toddler, I just walked away from my parents at the beach when I became displeased with the way things were going.

"Oh, just let him go," said my father. "He'll come back in a minute."

Hey, I was out of there, no problem. The police later found me because I had on a beach robe made with many colors that was easily identifiable. My parents had been frantic, but I was unfazed. I had merely enjoyed the walk on the beach and the view from the pier.

My sister and I shared the same room down the hall from the bathroom. When I felt the call of nature in the darkest part of the night, I would slip out of my covers and feel my way to Francesca's bed. (She slept dead to the world and for 30 years never knew about this.) I would crawl under her covers, pull down my diaper and snuggle up to her and then wee-wee in her bed. It was too dark and scary for me to trek to the bathroom (even though it wasn't too far for me to escape to Mrs. Ball's apartment). Every morning I would wake up with a dry diaper and she would get in trouble for wetting the bed. As I stared out blankly from my baby bed, Mom would gently reprimand her. My eyes said it all, "Don't be too hard on her, Mom—she can't help it." Truer words were never spoken. When we were in our 30s, I finally confessed my nightly trysts to Francesca, and she was stunned. Her whole life she'd thought that she had been the victim of a weak bladder condition during childhood, only to find out—I had struck again.

4

MRS. BALL

THROUGHOUT MY LIFE MANY EXCEPTIONAL PEOPLE HAVE MADE influential appearances. These friends have tinted my views, colored my soul, and sweetened the pot of life. Mrs. Gertrude Ball was certainly one of those people. The careful placement of her hands; the tilt of her unpretentious, yet self-possessed face; the timeless clear-blue eyes always looking at me...looking deep into me with respect and interest. How I revered Mrs. Ball.

She makes me breathless just remembering her. The impact she had on my life cannot be measured. Sometime during our 28-year friendship, I realized the scope of her former wealth and social prominence; however, those things meant nothing to me as a small boy.

Mrs. Ball came into my life when my family lived in a multi-floored tenement building in New Jersey. To most observers this substandard patchwork of poor humanity could be quickly dismissed as quite forgettable. As undesirable as it was, however, it housed one (and maybe more) top-of-the-line items—the elegant and truly remarkable Mrs. Ball (never Gertrude).

After the stock market crash in 1929, Mrs. Ball's financially devastated family moved to our tenement building. She came from wealth, and then married into the untold riches of the Ball family. The countless hours she shared with me are among my favorite memories.

To me she was a queen, always proper with a dainty handbag, gloves, a mustard-seed necklace, and perhaps a lovely, light-blue wool suit gracing her statuesque body. Everything mattered to her—the temperature, the dinner plans, the news, the state of affairs, but, best of all, I was important to her.

She was one of those people who really cared and listened in a nonjudgmental way to what I thought and said. I must have said a lot during those many years, but it is her conversations I frequently revive. She gave me the best gift anyone can give: her time.

We lived across the hall from one another, and when Mom came looking for me, she usually began at Mrs. Ball's apartment. Even as a little boy, the fabrics, choice of colors, and placement of her collectibles intrigued me. I was drawn to the opulence, to the fineness of it all. Family portraits on her apartment walls sternly surveyed the scene for untold years, making sure that family traditions continued. They did. She had elevated living to an art, even during the hard times, and hard times would be all she ever knew after the stock market crash.

This must have been hell for her, coming from a 35-bedroom Newport Rhode Island estate furnished with servants and a three-sided view of the ocean, but even in its diminished form she continued to live the dream and to approach life with an unyielding structure of morals, kindness, and grace. In many ways I am still influenced by memories of her. In particular I remember how she cared for her devastated husband with the gentleness of a surgeon.

"Oh, thank you! What lovely peaches," she would reply when her husband arrived from the store with unneeded and overly expensive items. I never saw her belittle him; or heard her slip in demeaning accusations of their financial inadequacies. She allowed him his dignity and pride. I watched her, listened to her, and loved her, and in turn I was educated in a remarkable way—I was given a glimpse of an angel. I miss you, Mrs. Ball.

5

BUGS

BEFORE SATELLITE DISHES, CABLE TELEVISION, AND EVEN VCRs, early morning television viewing was very limited, especially when you're an early rising three-year-old. My favorite Saturday morning television program was the *Modern Farmer*, which bird-chirped its theme song as the opening credits (letters made of ears of corn and other vegetables) scrolled up the screen at 5:00 a.m.

I was totally captivated with the sincere Farmer Cliff who hosted the show, a Mr. Greenjeans with laid-back class. Integrity oozed out of him. I had the living room to myself at that hour of the morning. Probably had the whole show to myself, too. In my pajamas, with my little legs stuck straight out on the couch, I would intently watch Farmer Cliff discuss farming matters.

My love for planting and farming I directly relate to the countless *Modern Farmer* episodes I viewed as a young, impressionable boy. Particularly impressive to my three-year-old mind was a *Modern Farmer* program that concentrated on bugs—bugs in the flour, bugs on apples, and bugs on corn. My empty stomach lurched when Farmer Cliff eased into the camera with a beautiful ear of corn, parted the wilted silks, fingered the papery shucks aside, and revealed a worm on the run. Trouble in paradise. To a city slicker, this was a revelation. After 30 minutes of pesticide information, Farmer Cliff had won me over. I was informed and prepared to meet the enemy.

It was the morning of New Year's Eve, and I had witnessed my first memory of mother's food-making mania. For an entire week our family routine had been disrupted with the preparations for the New Year's Eve party. We weren't neglected during this food-making frenzy, just attended to with the glazed eyes of someone who has other things on her mind. There were endless trips to the supermarket, and countless sacks of food dumped onto the kitchen counters.

These were the years before prepared party trays and catered treats, so the buying of the food was just the beginning. Every item had to be cleaned, cut up, mixed, sautéed, cooked, steamed, baked, cooled, iced, and arranged on a tray or in a bowl. This endeavor didn't go unnoticed by my curious eyes. The kitchen was already my favorite room in the house, and during the days preceding the big party, I dodged flying potato peels, was dusted by white flour sifting down on my head, and received numerous stove warnings.

Observing Mom's concentrated effort and devotion really made an impression on me. That woman could cook. At last, the afternoon arrived and with the millionth final touch in place, the table gloriously set, and the glare of tinfoiled dishes completely obscuring every flat surface in the kitchen and dining room, Mom went upstairs to collapse into a short nap/coma.

With the lull in activity, my overly active imagination kicked in. "Tony, Mommy really worked hard cooking all of this food, didn't she," I thought to myself. "And now she's resting up for the company. What if bugs get into the food while she's upstairs?"

Thank heavens for Farmer Cliff. I dragged a stool to the pantry and found the bug spray. I eased up the tinfoil from each dish and sprayed my heart out. When I was certain each dish was bug-free, I moved through the dense cloud of pesticide to report my good deed to Mom.

I eased Mom's bedroom door open and approached her still body. Only the rhythmic, soft wheezes elevating the cold washcloth on her head gave evidence of life. She was melted into that bed like a chocolate bar on a dashboard in July, her swollen feet splayed out like the dead. Boy, did I have good news for her.

I softly approached her covered head and whispered, "Buggies won't get your food Mommy...buggies won't get your food."

All in one motion her body jerked to life. She jack-knifed, sending the washcloth splat against the wall, and her perfectly straight legs arched off the bed like a gymnast on the pommel horse.

At first her fury was restrained. "Tony, what did you do?" she panted. With a proud lilt in my voice I replied, "Buggies won't get your food."

"WHAT?" she shrieked. And with surprising speed, she descended the stairs to examine her edible labors of love. Her piercing screams changed pitch as she wildly circled the table lifting the tinfoil and smelling each masterpiece. No doubt about it, no bugs.

My father skidded into the pandemonium, getting tearfully shouted instructions to "Get him out of my sight!" He jerked me up under his arm and hustled me out like a log as Mom lunged at me.

That night I got to go to Grandma's house for sanctuary, so I really lucked out. At least I enjoyed New Year's Eve. Years later I found out they wound up ordering pizza for the party. Did I kill bugs the next year? I don't think so.

6

POTATOHEAD

I WAS ALMOST FOUR IN 1953 WHEN MY FAMILY MOVED TO PASSAIC Avenue on the main drag of Passaic, New Jersey, an industrial town. It was like we'd died and gone to heaven. Modest single family homes with small, well-kept yards lined the streets and reflected the young families' pride at having moved up in the world. There were lots of kids, with plenty of youthful energy.

We quickly became the centerpiece of the pleasant, but plain, neighborhood. After all, we had the only house with a huge bay window showcasing the pink drapes Mom had so creatively selected. I remember people approaching the house to inquire about the interior decorations and carpet color (which was gray, of course; after all, it was the 1950s). Even as a three-year-old, I was impressed by its modern flair.

My mother directed my youthful energies (some say rambunctiousness) to a series of nursery schools and kindergartens. We had a mutual goal: she couldn't wait to get me off for the day, and I was always up for the adventure. Lots of our cousins and my sister and I went to Miss Canady's School, where old Miss "Potatohead" Canady ruled. Her beady eyes flashed out of sunken holes under the ledge of black eyebrows.

Not to be outdone, the eyelids screamed BLUE while drawing unneeded attention to the half-stuck-on false eyelashes. She had never missed her weekly hair appointment, whether she needed it or not, and must have preserved the perfect halo of elevated, ratted hair with a sheer scarf at night.

When the parents brought their little victims in for the day, Miss Canady would sweep open the door as if she were admitting royalty, many times even handing out fake lunch menus to the unsuspecting parents.

"Oh, yes, ravioli for lunch tomorrow," they would think. We knew differently. It was bologna sandwiches and always bologna sandwiches. As soon as the final parent had left, we were told in no uncertain terms to "Lie down and take a nap." Rather than intimidate us, she amused us in a terrifying way. On the one hand, we were scared of her and never told our parents about the bologna sandwiches and endless naps; on the other hand, we defied her by huddling in the corner of the dark "napping" room to laugh at Miss Potatohead.

I can still remember her silhouetted, broad frame spying at us in the doorway of the slightly stirring, blackened room. My cousins and I would clutch each other and snicker into our cupped hands. Even then the family humor carried us through.

7

TURD

NOTHING LIKE THIS SHOULD HAVE EVER HAPPENED THE FIRST DAY of school, especially to an optimistic five-year-old with first-day jitters and high expectations.

"Now, Tony, be Mommy's best boy. Mind the Sisters. Make Mommy and Daddy proud." Mommy kissed me goodbye as she leaned across the front seat of our blue-and-white Pontiac.

At last, the day had come when I could accompany my sister to real school. I was finally on my way, and I had it all figured out. After a few minutes of learning what the Sisters had to say, I would smile sweetly, roam around the room helping others, and eventually take possession of all the blocks. Talk about shattered dreams.

Mom was hardly out of sight when all hell broke loose. I knew the school routine; I had watched my sister's daily entrance into the school for years. First, the old witch would come out on the landing with a tarnished, ancient bell, raise it high over her head, and flail away. The rule was to freeze up like a bunch of statues and listen for the second ringing that signaled time to get in your own grade-level line. The third bell meant, "Start marching in." Silently, of course.

It all happened sometime between the second and third bell. Beth's brown hair was bouncing at an especially frantic pace as we perfected the straightest line imaginable.

"Not good enough, boys and girls," barked the Sister. "Straighter—one, right behind the other."

I aligned myself perfectly behind Beth and waited for the bends in the line to heal up. At first, I thought that Beth was going to get in a lot of trouble because her legs were twisted around and her hands were holding herself from some great emergency. But I tuned it out as I dreamed of the fun we were going to have, if we ever got inside the door.

Suddenly my left foot felt slightly warm and heavy. I glanced down at my feet and recoiled in horror to see a slimy brown mound on my new Buster Brown school shoes. The wet, tapered turd lay embedded in the shoestrings.

I instinctively jerked my leg out, launching that brown missile. A dull splat to David Jernigan's head was followed by piercing screams of fellow classmates declaring, "Tony's slinging shit, Tony's slinging shit!" David went down like the Hindenburg, and to a screaming audience.

In a blink of an eye I was jerked up and facing Sister Patricia Marie, the principal.

"Tony, how perfectly horrible, absolutely disgusting! What will your mother and father think of this? Nothing like this has ever, EVER happened here at Holy Innocents."

"But Sister—I just looked down and there it was. I didn't poop, really. It wasn't me. It had to be Beth. She was in front of me," I cried.

I was in a mess of trouble. They called my sister down to the office and she began sobbing. Why they involved her I have no idea. Francesca was in the dark about the whole thing.

I felt like I had three accusatory penguins facing me down.
The principal had her arms crossed, and each hand was hidden
in the wide black sleeves of her habit. The two other sisters
who had witnessed the event stood by. Even at that age I was
bound to tell the truth, so I just turned and stared them down
and fingered Beth as the culprit.

"Now, Tony, don't try to blame an innocent bystander. That
makes one transgression into two. What would Jesus think?"
glared Sister Patricia Marie. Her white, chafed hands flailed the
air.

"Sister...really, REALLY, I didn't do it.... Go smell her
butt and see if she did it," I pleaded. That seemed like the right
solution to me. Unbelievably, they did take my advice and
discovered the smelly truth. And so ended my first day of
kindergarten.

8

ARCANGELA

MY GRANDMOTHER WAS AN ANGEL AND HER NAME PROVED IT: Arcangela. As I remember her, she amazes me. She hadn't intended to marry my grandfather, Giovanni; however, certain murky family arrangements dragged Giovanni into the picture, and her true love faded to black.

In so many ways Arcangela could be the poster person for the typical Italian grandmother with a busy life of food, family, and the Catholic Church. She wasn't tall or short; she was just right for a boy to hug, just right for a boy's head to be nestled into her soft, warm, abundant embrace. Her intellect was acute, focused, and keen to the end.

When she passed away, I was devastated. She had been the cog in the wheel of my boyhood. Whenever I was in trouble, she would comfort me, feed me, and guide me, in that order.

I can remember many mischievous episodes and close calls that were mollified by her intervention, which usually went like this: I would come flying into her arms with trouble at my heels, and her accepting words would soothe me, "Tony, Tony, what's wrong? What happened?" After telling her the problem, she would absorb the event, say nothing, neither agreeing nor disagreeing with me. She just listened. Then she would rise to fix something to eat.

"Tony, do you want a meatball sandwich?" Of course, I never turned that down.

This was a classic ceremony. After my emotional story, the words hung in the air while Arcangela prepared the food. There was silence for the full impact of the predicament to sink in. I knew what was coming, the truth. I just waited to hear her take on the situation, and she was never wrong. By the time she set the plate before me, I had time to step to one side of the episode and see it through her eyes.

As I was comforted by the food, I was many times gently reprimanded by her words. She would ask me questions to help me see both sides, and then she gave her opinions on solving the problem. With my mouth full, and having said my part, I found it easy to accept the advice of an angel.

Many weekends I stayed with my grandmother. These were my favorite times. One spring Giovanni made wine in the basement of their house and dared anyone to be in the vicinity of his project. The dark corner of the cellar was stacked with his collection of vats, hoses, and unknown devices, all connected together for the purpose of making his precious wine.

My cousins and I knew we'd be drawn, quartered, killed, and our throats slit if we bothered his wine-making enterprise. According to some of the family, Giovanni loved too much; according to me, he was downright mean. I do know that all of us kids avoided him like the plague. My cousins were terrified of him, but for some reason I liked to incite him, on occasion.

One afternoon I let loose and kicked the shit out of Giovanni's wine vat, and hoses snaked out, spewing fermented juice all over the basement floor. I ran upstairs to Grandmother; my short life flashed before me.

I dived into Grandmother's lap and waited for the sparks to fly. We were on the third floor of the house and could hear his every curse, his every threat as Granddad stormed up the basement steps toward us. The foaming bull screamed in Italian something about "morto" and I knew I was dead.

He threw open Grandmother's bedroom door and lunged for me, trying to yank me from my grandmother's grip and a tug of war ensued. "Giovanni, Giovanni," my grandmother screamed, "what are you doing? Why are you grabbing Tony?" He let go and I snapped back into Grandma's possession.

"I know he went down there! I know it was Tony who destroyed my wine. I know he was monkeying around down there. It was him!" Grandfather's gnarly finger shook at me; his voice rattled the air. Grandmother turned to me and said, "Tony, did you go down and touch Grandpa's stuff?"

With my perfected innocent look, I said, "No, Grandma."

She glared at him and said, "See, he wouldn't lie. Now you get on down there and fix it." She grabbed me up and asked if I wanted a meatball sandwich. Of course I said, "Yes."

I settled into a chair around the kitchen table and watched Grandma make her specialty. I could hear the still raging bull cleaning my mess below as Grandma approached me with the sandwich. She placed the dish before me and gently raised my face in her soft, warm hands. "Tony, it's not good to lie. Now you tell Grandma the truth. Were you playing in the wine cellar?"

"But, I didn't mess with it, Grandma."

"Now, Tony, it's not good to lie, and to Grandma of all people. Don't lie to Grandma now. Did you touch Grandpa's things?"

I looked up from the untouched sandwich with tears in my eyes, and she just kissed the tears away and whispered, "GOOD!"

9

DANCE

ABOUT THIS TIME, IT WAS DECIDED THAT MY SISTER SHOULD TAKE
some tap lessons at Miss Connie's dance studio. In Passaic,
New Jersey, one didn't have many choices of dance studios
and besides, all of my cousins took lessons from Miss Connie.
No one thought their kid would be the next Gwen Verdon or
Juliette Prowse, so it was fine enough as long as they learned
how to do a kick, a ball change, and a time step.

Every Saturday morning my mother would dutifully gather
us up, my sister with her patent-leather bag containing her tutu
and tap shoes, and me armed with comic books.

Speaking of comic books, Miss Connie looked like two
cartoon characters that had been split in half at the waist and
reassembled to make one hideous creature. Her top half was
her pride and joy, having been modified to look like Liz Taylor/
Marilyn Monroe and malnourished enough to pass an anorexia
test. That half of her torso was topped with flaming-red, wiry
hair that reached alarming heights due to heavy ratting and
layers of Suave hairspray. Her Marilyn Monroe aspirations were
satisfied by the black beauty spot that grew and migrated on
her face with every passing year. Miss Connie's Liz Taylor

imitation was sadly reflected in her advanced eyelashes and self-confidence.

I assume she never looked at herself in the wall of mirrors that ringed the studio, or, if she did, she must have wondered at the apparent distortions in them. Like the fun-house wavy mirrors that make fat figures slim, hers made slim figures fat. Little did she know that she could have earned a lot more money as a freak in the circus.

Her lower half was an eye-opening collection of swollen bumps like sandbags hanging off her ass. She sported her enormous butt around with exaggerated swirls and her approach could be heard as her black tights rubbed together and made scraping, raspy sounds announcing her arrival. I always prayed that she wouldn't demonstrate a kick toward me, revealing the hidden shock of her thighs under her skirt.

As observers to my sister's exposure to dance culture, Mom and I perched on folding chairs along the wall. A beat-up piano sat off to the side with Miss Riley patiently waiting to bang away with the next exaggerated beat. The kids were all lined up, mostly girls and perhaps two boys, and we know what they turned out to be.

Miss Connie would endlessly repeat directions and demonstrate moves only to be disappointed in the dancers' progress. I would become annoyed because it looked so easy and frequently jump up and say, "This is what she means. Here's how to do it."

Before long, I was in one of Miss Connie's recitals and didn't mind it too much because I only had to take dance class one out of the four weeks. Actually, I got some good training there and later went on to better studios.

10

Fire Drill

Our school, Holy Innocents, was old, but not as old as the nuns. These were the pre-laughing nun days, just a bunch of sore winners going to Heaven, and it sure was costing them. The "Singing Nun" was as fictitious as Pinocchio as far as I was concerned. I hovered over class work from kindergarten through sixth grade with my extrasensory antenna up, scanning for the Dominican Terrors. Very rarely did they approach undetected.

First, there was the smell of starched linen that cut through the kid mildew-and-sweat cloud that clung to the rows of students. And then there were the swishes of stirring air that announced their arrival seconds before the black leather shoes eased into view next to my desk.

Punishment was so simple for them because they weren't encumbered with issuing warnings or sending letters home to concerned parents. They didn't even have to come armed to your desk. They would just snatch up your own ruler and beat the hell out of your hands, pop the ruler back onto your desk, tuck their arms into the sleeves of their habits, and float away with an air of dutiful satisfaction.

I never really hated them, though. I always knew they loved me, thought I was cute, and reserved major capital punishments for others, even though I most certainly deserved it, if anybody did.

Just picture the hours of coexistence with robed black-and-white creatures who were beyond reproach, had emotional gauges set on "stern," and never smiled or laughed with other nuns, even in an unguarded moment.

What color was their underwear? I always wondered. Allen Durwich and I devised a plan to find out—"Fire Drill!"

In elementary school little things can be blown out of proportion—made so explosively big. Take, for instance, the common fire drill. In our case we were shushed and manhandled by Sister Crecentia's vice-grip fingers at the fire escape landing that launched us out onto the wire see-through fire escape stairs. The whole thing was vibrating with kids scrambling to exit the building. Talk about fun and scary, this was heaven to a kid.

Several Sisters would accompany us as we flowed down to the yard below. Allen and I just knew if we could tear around the next bend in the fire escape and look up, there would be a magical moment of discovery. The underwear question would be answered. We hoped for the cloak of confusion, noise, and squealing fear to disguise our investigation. This scientific inquiry had to be perfectly timed. We pushed and positioned ourselves as fast as we could to the next most advantageous spot on the landing. From there we would crane our eyes up trying to see anything, until we were bumped along by the swell of escaping kids.

We never saw anything, by the way, except an irate Sister Leo George at the bottom of the fire escape who jerked us up, slapped us around, and called us "perverts."

To this day I still wonder, "What color is their underwear?"

11

RUNAWAY

AT HOLY INNOCENTS WE ATE IN THE BOWELS OF THE SCHOOL. The lunchroom was on the lowest level and was awash with navy-and gray-clad kids scurrying around carrying enormous beige trays. There wasn't a speck of yellow, red, or green, just the dull end of the color spectrum with the ever-present accents of white-and-black gesturing nuns directing the confusion.

Forget about choices at lunch. We ate whatever was dished out, and that day the menu included vegetable soup, fruit cocktail, saltine crackers, white milk, and a fork-smashed peanut butter cookie the size of a saucer.

I carefully balanced my tray and settled in next to my friends from the third grade. The newness of school had long ago dimmed, and, as a second grader, I was already becoming rather complacent to the whole scene—only ten more years to go.

I spooned the soup with gusto trying to avoid the caved-in green peas that seemed so plentiful and used a saltine cracker to temporarily hold back the green tide so that I could get to the ground beef and potato chunks sunken near the murky bottom. This took concentration and time. I downed the carton of milk, glanced at the fruit cocktail, and fished out the deep-red cherry half. Those were like prizes. As I reached for the cookie, it occurred to me that my class had left for the playground. I quickly opened the small paper napkin and carefully wrapped the peanut butter cookie, pocketed it to be enjoyed later that afternoon, and hurried out. To my horror I saw that my classmates were gone, snatched up by our teacher, Sister Cleo Grace, and probably already digging out workbooks and pencils for afternoon arithmetic.

The Sisters were eternally vigilant for anything out of the ordinary and I never wanted to draw attention to myself for fear of getting into a bind with them. So I forced myself to leave the playground in a disguised, spirited walk rather than a flat-out run, but I knew I was in for it and was preparing myself for the worst.

The journey consisted of two flights of dipped and worn stairs. I slid my hand up the railing as far as it would go, and then pulled myself up at a radical angle. Hand over hand I pulled myself toward certain disaster. As I ascended the stairs, the greasy lunchroom smells lessened, but the reality of my predicament increased. Old Sister Cleo Grace was surely waiting for me.

I knew why she'd become a nun. Where else could she wear a tent and get away with it? But even the heavy, black cloth couldn't hide the three tons of pumpkins she had hidden underneath it. When she stood in front of me, I couldn't see anything but a looming and impressive Sister Cleo Grace. She lumbered down our hallways like an enormous tightrope walker. With her puffed-out arms skewed at right angles to the ground and our class following her, like a string of uniformed ants snaking along behind her, she made an impressive general.

Sister Cleo Grace's rosary and cross would have swayed back and forth as she walked except for the fact that they were usually trapped between the two fleshy mountains that were supposed to be disguised behind the starched, white bib. I always wondered if they charged her double for her habits. A family of dwarfs probably lived under its voluminous folds.

She would collapse into her oversized chair after lunch just to catch her breath from the lunchroom journey and we would draw a sigh of short-lived relief. Soon, however, she would soon come back to her senses and begin barking out class assignments.

In the meantime, I had finished my trek and stood trembling outside the door to my classroom listening to resounding threats that issued out of Sister Cleo Grace's cave-mouth, "The next kid who comes in here gets his ass beat."

That's the way I remember it, but she probably said it differently. However she said it, it meant that I was about to be walking into a bottom-popping fury. The next kid was going to be jerked up to the front of the room, forced to drop his pants, and have the hell beat out of him with a board. I decided right then that "the next kid" wasn't going to be me. There was no way I was going in there. I mean, there was no way possible to hide your crack in any shape or form, so I took off.

Somehow I managed to escape out the side door and ran to the refuge of Pat's Sweet Shop, which for 21 years had been opportunistically located across from Holy Innocents School. Skinny and slow-moving old Pat was mopping the cracked black-and-white-tiled floor when I burst through the door, seeking asylum. This was the 1950s and, as unbelievable as it sounds today, he allowed me to call a cab after hearing my breathless excuse.

"The phones in the school are out, Pat. I'm sick and need to go home, and the principal told me to come here to call Mom."

The cab arrived quickly, but it dawned on me that I really didn't want to go home to be yelled at, so I told the cab driver to take me to my grandmother's home.

Arcangela, my beloved grandmother, welcomed me with opened arms. I always went to her in times of trouble. She thanked and paid the driver, and rested her warm hand on my shoulder as we climbed the stairs to her home. The first thing she wanted to know was if I was okay and she patiently listened as I spilled my lies about being sick and being sent home for the day.

"Would you like something to eat?" she offered.

Of course I said, "Yes." As we were hypnotized by the afternoon soap operas, I devoured my second lunch of the day and whiled away a luscious afternoon with my favorite person. Hours passed and I was having the best time when she mentioned that it was 5:00 p.m. and did I feel well enough to stay for dinner? "Oh, YES," I cried.

"Then better call Mommy and ask her if it's okay and to pick you up later," she called from the kitchen. I went to the phone and held down the receiver and made a pleading fake call home. "She said, 'Okay.'"

I had no idea of the turmoil spinning on the other side of town. "Kidnapped," "murdered," "lost"—all sorts of predicted headlines were being whispered ever more frantically in conjunction with "poor little Tony." Police had been out looking for me since I hadn't returned from lunch and my parents and relatives were half-crazy with fear. My Grandmother and I were busy making ravioli.

After dinner I curled up on the sun porch to rest and Arcangela cleaned up the dishes. About 9:00 p.m. my exhausted father arrived and pushed through the front door of Grandmother's house.

"Dear, whatever is wrong? You look like you've seen a ghost."

With a dramatic gesture he pointed Grandmother to the couch. (After all, everyone should be sitting when they hear bad news.)

"Momma, I've got some bad news for you." Her eyes welled up with tears as she searched his face for the dreaded bad news. Oh, how Dad hated to tell Arcangela that her favorite grandchild was missing.

He gathered himself and with measured resignation announced, "It's Tony. We can't find Tony. We think he's been kidnapped." He sobbed and he fell into her arms.

"What? Kidnapped? Missing? He's been here with me all afternoon!" she declared. "He's in the sun porch taking a nap."

I awoke to the relieved cries and kisses of my dad. "Tony, Tony, we were so worried!" He held me tight. I clutched his neck and told my story about what I had heard outside the classroom that day. He cried as he squeezed me, the terror of possibly losing a child somewhat subsiding. I knew he had to be furious and relieved, but he listened to my side of the story. I'll always love him for listening to me then.

He gathered me up and returned me to our house to the relieved cheers of Mom and the other relatives who had gathered to receive any impending bad news. The next day he paid a visit to the school and "straightened things out."

Sister Cleo Grace never got out of hot water on that one. After that year, she mysteriously disappeared from the school faculty. Speaking of hot water, the peanut butter cookie stain in my uniform pants pocket remained a permanent reminder of that fateful day.

12

SHERRY

MRS. BROSHELL'S LUCK HAD FINALLY RUN OUT. HER FIFTH AND final child, a girl, was (to put it mildly) a disappointment. The baby's name was Sherry, daringly named for a savory, after-dinner wine that provides a fragrant exclamation point to a fine meal. With such a classy name—so expectant, so full of meaning—Sherry would certainly be another delightful addition to the Broshell family. Maybe she would even be as pretty as her older sister, Barbara.

Perhaps poor Mrs. Broshell had forgotten the formula. After the birth of delicate Barbara, three baby boys had followed, providing the family with three junior policemen who resembled their policeman dad. Maybe she had simply used up all her good genes. Whatever genes were scraped together to make Sherry produced a desperately ungainly girl who required limitless attention.

Unfortunately, Sherry was smart, or at least adequate in the IQ department. I stress "unfortunately smart" because she was all too aware of the unkind discrepancies between herself and her sister. Sherry was soon handing her clothes "up" to Barbara. She wore the Tom-Boy brand of short-legged Jeans for Husky Girls (when she was allowed to wear jeans). In the third grade, she was slipped an upper graders' school desk to accommodate her expanding figure.

She really was gifted at infuriating her schoolmates. And, of course, we loved to have someone to taunt. Everyone has someone in their school memories who picked boogers and either ate them or sported them on a threatening, slick finger. The fastest I ever moved was when Sherry and her waving wet finger came lunging at us boys huddled in a pack on the playground. We scattered like pinballs.

The booger trick always got our attention, but that took a back seat in the eighth grade to her new trick, blowjobs. Ever more desperate for status and ever more aware of her lackluster appearance, Sherry sprayed her thin, mole-colored hair firmly enough to withstand the rigors of behind-the-stage-curtain extra curricular activities. Only the truly curious boys ventured into that scene. To be sure, the ones who did reported back to the rest of us with pride, but, according to the survivors, it was not worth the fear of reporting it to Monsignor Vight at confession.

Since our school was located on the grounds of Holy Innocents church, religion was never far away. I really miss those days when the massive, carved front doors of the church were left unlocked for all to come and worship. No matter the time of day, people could enter the church, plunk down a dime for a candle, and send up prayers to the heavenly listeners.

One blustery autumn afternoon Sherry Broshell scrambled into the church, barely jerking her flapping coat-tail from being caught in the wind-sucked door. She paid her dime and lit a candle. Hers was added to the trough of countless others, some flickering, others mere lifeless stubs, at the foot of the Blessed Mother statue. Sherry had been relieved to see that she was almost alone in the church. Even as a eighth grader, she was scared of the Bleeding Christ on the Cross, the Blessed Virgin Mary, and just about everything else in there. Hell, we all were. Our whole lives we were exposed to bleeding crowns of thorns and leaking abdomen wounds from lifelike statues of Christ on the Crucifix. It could be terrifying to a kid.

The stillness, the incense, the thick, heavy air filling the spaces between massive marble pillars that shadowed an elaborate, 50-foot fresco of Biblical stories was enough to elevate worshipers' souls and to remind them that others, too, had lived less than perfect lives. Sherry knelt at the foot of the Blessed Virgin Mary, her thick ankles crossed and her emotional, guilty eyes longingly searching Mary's face for some sign of forgiveness or at least understanding of her adolescent pranks.

The Blessed Virgin Mother was the focal point of the church. From a commanding pedestal she watched over the worshipers where her beacon eyes stared down even the most repentless sinner. A rich blue, velvet curtain eased around behind her setting off her gilded robes and heavenly spotlights zeroed in on her from above. She was magnificent. No doubt about it, she was the Mother of God.

Sherry felt unhurried in her prayers and at ease to elaborate about her troubles—when a miracle occurred. Sherry saw the Blessed Mary move. Just a friendly tilt, a reassuring bow it seemed. And then, she spoke. The Blessed Mother of God spoke to her.

"Sherry, everything will be all right," she said in a throaty voice. The Virgin Mary never spoke again. At least Sherry didn't hear it because she flew out of the church screaming hysterically, her shoulder bag floating behind her.

No one questioned her story. Catholics know these kinds of saintly interventions occasionally occur and most pray to be so lucky. Instantly she became elevated to the top of the charts as far as popularity was concerned. Fellow students nodded reverently and genuflected to her in the halls. For five months Sherry's celebrity grew. The town was saving to send her to meet the Pope in Rome. She was selected to be May Queen, and, best of all, she was immersed in non-stop attention. Every girl dreamed of being the May Queen because she would crown the Blessed Virgin Mary in front of hundreds of people.

All eyes were on Sherry as she led the procession of children dressed in white dresses and suits. All eyes were on her because she looked like a Macy's Thanksgiving Parade balloon— earthbound, too heavy to fly. Her enormous white, bride-like dress demanded attention, as well as three seats at the banquet that afternoon. But nothing could stop her now. Her words were considered. Her opinions mattered. She was something special.

However, during these five glorious months, the church janitor had been suffering terrible pangs of guilt. After many sleepless nights he finally came forward with the truth. One Friday afternoon after the May crowning, he entered the confessional with Monsignor Vight. Overcome with remorse, he confessed that he had tilted the Virgin Mary while cleaning her and had spoken the holy words from beyond the grave. His prank had given Sherry her 15 minutes of fame, 10,000 fold. Andy Warhol would have been impressed.

13

JACKET

MY FATHER'S CONSTRUCTION BUSINESS WAS THRIVING WHEN we moved into a beautiful ranch house on a corner, ¾-acre lot in West Caldwell, New Jersey. I was ten and beginning to dream about being a star. My exposure to dance and modeling whetted an insatiable appetite for performing and the recognition it brought. Some would say I started early.

In 1951, when I was one, my mom entered my picture in the Gerber Baby contest, and I won for that year. Some time after that I signed with the Mel Malone Agency to arrange modeling jobs for me and for several years, I modeled for Best and Company, located next to St. Patrick's Cathedral in New York City. When they were bought out, I began a long career with Lord and Taylor as a runway model for the new lines of fashions.

At an age when most boys were concerned with getting a new football jersey or a basketball hoop, I was busy pursuing my dream to be a star. I loved every minute of being a model, from riding the bus or taking the subway there, to striding down the runway watching people watch me. I had thick, dark hair, hazel eyes, and a strong self-confidence and relished being the center of attention everywhere I went. Once in a hotel lobby when I was very young, I just belted out a Broadway tune to the delight of passersby. At least that's how I remember it; Mom simply recalls that I frequently brought new acquaintances to meet them wherever we went. I was always meeting new friends.

Whatever I was told to wear, or however I was asked to pose, I gladly complied because deep inside I knew these were the requirements for becoming known; this was paying the dues. I had already logged years of observing the wealthier people, the upper echelon, and classier people, like Mrs. Ball.   I was fascinated with the lifestyle of the rich—how they conducted themselves, how they set a dinner table, and how they acted. Even as a child I was keen on placing myself in the right place in order to make my dreams come true. I realized I couldn't stay home expecting stars and dreams to come knocking at my door and all of a sudden have my dreams fulfilled. I knew I had to do the knocking.

I remember a Thanksgiving family gathering where our entire family of aunts, uncles, grandparents, and cousins were watching television, trying to recover from the midday feast. We lay about the living room watching a show about Beverly Hills with its mansions and Rolls-Royces.   Huge iron gates slowly opened so the magnificent white Rolls could glide up the circular driveway to the hand-carved double doors of the mansion. I can clearly remember this moment as if it happened yesterday. I just turned to everyone and said, "Someday I'm going to live there."

A long moment of limp-jawed silence was followed by eruptive hilarity. Screams of laughter filled the room and Uncle Joe asked, "Well, Tony, what do you intend to do? You know it costs a lot of money to live out there. What will you do?"

I straightened my back and declared, "I'm going to be a star." There, I'd said it. The truth was out. Even as a young person, I knew my destiny.

What I didn't realize then could fill a book. Uncle Joe was correct about the cost of living in Beverly Hills, as I later discovered, but he neglected to mention the other costs involved, or that money can't buy fulfillment or peace of mind. It was a lesson long in coming: money doesn't necessarily bring happiness.

But back to the West Caldwell move. After an interview with Sister Jimma and much anxiety about my academic future, I was admitted into Saint Ignatius Catholic School. Maybe it was my age or some other circumstance, but this became the first time in my life that I had to make some adjustments. I was going into the sixth grade and at this point I knew my sexuality was being questioned. I wasn't interested in or good at sports, which drew questionable attention to my apparent deficiencies from my schoolmates.

By the way, with the exception of my granddad, Giovanni, no other relative ever seemed to care that I didn't sweat with the football team or wrestle with ear guards strapped to my head, like all the other boys. I was Tony, cut from a different cloth, a fabric cherished by my family and friends.

Boarding the bus to a new school the first time can be a singular experience. Most people have probably forgotten. I had dressed with much trepidation for my first day of school at Saint Ignatius and was carefully groomed for that first, great impression all the way down to my new three-ring notebook filled with Blue Horse paper. Completing the look was a gold jacket from a modeling session at Best and Company. I thought it was so in and fashionable, and I was without friends this first day and needed a bolster from some high fashion. Besides, I was secretly terrified of getting on the school bus.

Waiting for the bus gave me time to assess the situation and to plan an alternative path to acceptance. I couldn't count on sports—that common masculine link—to bond me to the other guys; I would have to hone my sense of humor to create an aura of magnetic attraction. This became my plan for acceptance.

It's quite possible that my gold jacket was the first and last gold jacket ever to be worn on that bus. The other kids viewed me as an alien, a complete foreigner that had dropped in from Mars. I arrogantly considered their jeers as indications they were ignorant, fashion-challenged creeps, and quickly chose a seat. I forced my gaze out the smeary window and acted as if I was viewing something utterly fascinating in hopes of diverting attention from the blinding gold reflection emanating from me. I prayed the unwanted attention would dissipate and I would be ignored.

This strategy probably would have worked if the little girl in the seat in front of me hadn't turned around, staring with the whites of her eyes showing all around, and thrown up on my new gold jacket. It was not a pretty sight, grape juice and more sliding down the front of my fashion statement.

Unsolicited reviews roared from the crowd, "Yaaaaa...it looks better with puke all over it!" I could have died.

Over a short period of time and with some toned-down fashion modifications, I calmed my jets, told my stories, became interested in my new friends and soon had everyone on my side. During the sixth grade I began to feel the power of seduction: the seduction of the theater, dance, music, fashion, and the stardust on my shoulders.

During this time, I began working with Helen Merritt in her New York penthouse studio located down from the Dakota on West 72nd Street.

My parents always supported us (along with my sister, Francesca, we had a new brother, Greg) with our dreams and would bring me into New York and wait while I had my 45-minute lesson. But I'm sure that it was not their dream to raise a kid like the one I began turning into. By the end of the sixth grade I was probably the most rambunctious, rude child around. I had auditioned and won some parts in minor productions along with increased modeling opportunities and simply thought I was a cat's ass.

At a concerned family meeting, it was pointed out that they wanted a behaved child, not a cat's ass, although they said this in kinder words. In his sweet, understated way, Dad said, "You know Tony, we have to come up with an alternative plan here for schooling. I think you're a bit out of control."

I could see the wisdom in this, too, because I thought that I was a bit off the wall and my poor parents couldn't control me any more. We decided on Devonshire School for boys. I went willingly and with an overheard conversation ringing in my ears, "One of two things are going to happen at this school. Either they'll break Tony or Tony will break them."

14

DEVONSHIRE

FOR THE NEXT TWO YEARS I ATTENDED DEVONSHIRE SCHOOL, AN all-boys boarding school located about an hour from my home in West Caldwell. My attendance there was a joint decision between my folks and myself, and I willingly agreed to go.

I didn't feel that I had been thrown out to the wolves, and I arrived there with more confidence than when I started at Saint Ignatius. I felt good about walking into this school because, at this point, my photograph was in a couple of magazines, and it was so much easier being accepted in a new environment when I had an edge on the competition. Still, the recognition and acceptance were limited and weren't based on intimacy or friendships. I was not a favorite, and I very badly needed to be.

Compared to the Catholic schools I had attended, the courses there were very difficult, and I started to fail. Devonshire was a boarding school and we were allowed to go home on the weekend—unless we were failing any subject.

During this period of adjustment, I thought for sure that my winning personality and smile would win my weekend freedom; however, along with about ten other sad souls, I remained on Friday nights and suffered through study hall for hours on Saturday morning until my grades finally came up. After the Saturday study hall incarceration, we were set free until Sunday night, when we were required to be back on campus.

One of my fondest memories during this academic disgrace was of my dad's Friday visits. He took the time to encourage and support me during my uncertain times at Devonshire by driving an hour after work on Friday nights to have dinner with me even though he would have to come get me the next afternoon after study hall. We would go to a nice restaurant and talk over a fine meal. These visits banished my loneliness. I felt special: he had skipped the end-of-the-week pleasures of relaxing with the family at home to come keep me company. Because of that I felt warm and loved. Whenever I got down on myself and believed I couldn't continue there, I would remember his comforting words. At a Friday night dinner I had said, "You know, Dad, I'm so sorry I'm such a screw-up and you have to come here. I apologize. I wouldn't blame you if you didn't love me."

"Tony, do you know how much I love your mother?" His kind face and words reached out to me across the table.

"Yes," I replied.

"You're so much like her; how could I not love you?"

I felt bathed in love. I felt that I could do anything. People need these words said to them throughout life in order to get over hurdles. With his 100 percent support, I threw myself into the classroom challenges and actually made the honor roll and became the school mascot.

15

MASCOT

I WAS CHOSEN TO BE MASCOT BOTH YEARS I ATTENDED DEVONSHIRE School, and I had to go to all of the football games. This put me in the spotlight every Friday night. Dressed in a white woolly sweater with a crimson "D" on my chest, white pants and shoes, I stood for Devonshire's paradoxical desire for victory—to crush the opponents, yet to win in a dignified all-American way.

On those magical Friday nights, goosebumps rippled up my arms as the National Anthem was played and the flag rose slowly to the top of the flagpole. The marching band pumped up and down and around before finally filing into the bleachers. The band members were in another world with secret, furtive insider's jokes sparking from member to member, even when blowing their lungs out while connected to a 75-pound tuba.

Oh well, no one had a better mission than I. With my lively hazel eyes, white teeth, and a relatively small, energetic stance, I could flash a smile that would light up the nose-bleed seats. Unlike the cheerleaders who had to constantly perform structured routines with practiced precision, I had the run of the place. I was in ad-lib heaven. Whatever came to my little mind was instantly and energetically pursued.

Most of the time I didn't know if we were winning or losing. I just leaped about longingly, imploring the sea of fans to cheer the team to victory. Blinding lights illuminated me from overhead; cheering fans were just a dark blur of bundled-up color. As I turned my squinting face into it to yell, "GIVE ME A 'D'," I assumed I looked heavenly in my angelic, pure-white uniform. During kickoffs, extra point tries, and dramatic wins, I was tossed around like a doll by the heftier cheerleaders, to my absolute delight.

Grandpa Giovanni kindly chauffeured me to a game one brisk Friday night in October and I'll never forget it; neither will anyone else who was there that night. Granddad was mentally losing it and had been the focus of muted concern for years before that night. He drove his huge green Pontiac without resolve or decisive motions and to his dismay, many times he arrived somewhere he hadn't intended.

Besides his hobby of making wine in the basement, he busied himself during his later years dismantling every doorknob in his house, to "fix" it. In the workroom on an old table lay the skeletal remains of 16 doorknobs, locks and bolts in a hopeless tangle, never to be reunited with their rightful companions. I always practiced extreme self-control before using the bathroom in his house because, without the doorknob, the three-inch hole in the door left little to the imagination of my curious, peeping cousins.

But back to the game: it was common in the early 1960s for the football bleachers to be on a hill and for cars to line up next to the bleachers. Half-hearted fans could stay warm in their cars, maybe getting out to walk around, grab a hotdog from the vendor, or kiss a girl friend during the halftime.

On this particular October evening, we won. After the exhilarating winning-finish to the game, I climbed into Giovanni's green bomb parked on the hill next to the bleachers. His swollen fingers fumbled with the worn key and upon hearing "Old Goose" jump to life, he jammed his foot on the accelerator and floored it.

Thank God everyone got out of the way. With clumps of dirt flying behind us, we were catapulted out of the darkness into the light of the playing field, where we began a circling odyssey. Obviously, he didn't know where the road was.

All exiting of the stadium ceased. Even the losing team stopped walking off the field to stare in disbelief at the out-of-control car. More than once I became airborne off the front seat. Bouncing about, I occasionally caught a glimpse of an accusing crimson-and-white pompom frantically pointing our way. We sped alarmingly where no vehicle had ever gone: off the hill, through the players' benches, and onto the track that circled the entire football field. Giovanni must have temporarily thought he was in the Indianapolis 500 because he lapped the field repeatedly. Didn't he realize the scenery hadn't changed much?

By now, the noise easily exceeded the loudest roar from the game. People were going wild trying to flag down the crazed, circling fan. I crunched onto the floorboard out of sight as soon as we hit the smooth track and kept yelling, "Go through the woods, Grandpa. Go through the woods and hit the road."

He didn't say one word. He just kept going around and around like the Energizer Bunny. From my position under the dashboard, Giovanni looked like a Roman coin; his stark profile completely overpowered by an advanced hook nose and no lips, just a slit...not exactly Mario Andretti.

Finally, I grabbed the steering wheel and poked my head up enough to see a little woods fast approaching and aimed for it. Some small trees were sacrificed during our escape, but we eventually emerged onto the road.

"There, Grandpa," I panted.

And he just said, "Thank you."

16

BARRY

I WAS BOTH MASCOT OF THE SCHOOL'S FOOTBALL TEAM AND THE constant companion of its captain, Barry Clayton. Even though I was a mere eighth grader and this guy was a junior, we became very close. Like all boys this age, we were beginning to define our sexuality; I don't know if Barry later became gay, but he found me very attractive and hotly pursued me. Homosexuality wasn't discussed then, nor was there information easily available about it. I only knew that I enjoyed his attentive protectiveness and thought it wonderful to be at his side.

We were practically inseparable. Barry would walk me back to the underclassman's dorm after I practiced the piano in the music room. Many times he'd come early just to hear me practice, and I thrived in his fascinated obsession with me. When we went to basketball games, he always sat next to me and made me feel secure and warm.

I don't know if all the things that would come later stemmed from this relationship, but I have been very fortunate that the men in my life, the ones who found me attractive, were extremely kind, very supportive, and solicitous in their attention towards me. I think that's what has made the whole homosexual experience so appealing to me, and I wouldn't change it at all.

God gifted me with the right amount of masculinity. I was not effeminate at all as a child. My mom's clothes didn't tempt me, except one Halloween when I dressed up as a beauty queen and felt decidedly uncomfortable all night long. But I did have that touch of feminine qualities that guys found very attractive. I was ethereal looking, not handsome. It was a pretty, but still masculine look. At a boarding school where you couldn't get your hands on a girlfriend, my look was very appealing.

So Barry and I had a courtship. I don't think he would even remember it. Well, maybe he would remember it, because we did hold hands at times, and he was extremely protective of me. If someone was critical of me, Barry was right there to defend me. It was strange that our relationship was not exposed, noticed, or ridiculed by the other boys. Our fling lasted about a year, and we separated only because I choose to change schools and go to Cambridge Academy.

My impending departure was unwelcome news to Barry, and he tried to change my mind. Our farewell wasn't passionate, but it did include some hugging and petting. Even though we had a genuine love for each other, I never kept in touch with him after I moved to Cambridge Academy. I guess destiny pulled each of us in different directions.

17

FUNERAL

ABOUT THIS TIME MY GRANDFATHER, GIOVANNI, PASSED AWAY AND I began bracing myself for his funeral. Our Italian family was notorious for having theatrical wakes and funerals, so much so that my mother and other family members would watch the proceedings with pen and paper close at hand, to write up Oscar nominations for Best Leading Actor, Best Scream, Best Floral Arrangement, and so on.

This last award had nothing to do with floral beauty. It had to do with the ostentatiousness of the arrangements. For example, symbolism was big during the sixties, and a favorite funeral floral display of the time had broken ladders jutting out of them. The broken rung indicated which child had left this earth.

Huge mums were also used to create enormous clocks showing the exact moment of the deceased's departure from this earth (or maybe the exact time the departed arrived in Heaven). The hands of the clock were made of stiff cattails from nearby marshes. These were a big hit at Giovanni's funeral. No matter where the mourners sat in the cavernous funeral home, there were floral clocks visible with the valuable information "10:45" on them.

A floral phone arrangement caught on quickly in New Jersey. Some say it originated in the South. Dyed black and white carnations were arranged to form a realistic rotary dial phone and across it stretched a satin banner declaring, "Jesus called. Giovanni answered." We loved it. The southern version of this arrangement incorporated a plastic toy phone with the handpiece dangling off the hook as if the deceased had been "called upstairs" mid-conversation.

Off to the sides and in the back of the funeral home were the largest, most fabulous ensembles. Some resembled fountains made entirely of flowers. Many were elevated on pedestals to give them that Roman touch.

If the deceased happened to be named for a Saint, the hall looked like a chess set with endless statues of St. Joseph or whomever standing ready among the greenery. Bleeding hearts had seen their better days and were too common; however, some clever florist devised an updated version that looked really bloody. There was a bit of a revival for them. Indeed, the Rose Bowl Parade had nothing on us. During the three-day wake, all the arrangements had to be viewed and sympathy cards checked so that the Oscar nominations reflected absolute integrity and accuracy.

Over the years we increased the number of Oscars to include Best Supporting Cast and Best Performance given by a woman and a man. Not to sound too disrespectful, but my family lived to be very, very old, and at that time we hadn't dealt with any tragedies. Up until that point, everyone had lived a good, long life and should have welcomed death.

When Giovanni died, the word got to his brother, Uncle Tony, who lived in Brooklyn. Legend had it that a nasty disagreement (over a quarter) had caused a 26-year spat between the brothers, during which time neither had spoken to the other. Grandpa was 81 when he died, and Uncle Tony was 86. Both brothers lived out their last years without their marbles all in a row, as they say.

Upon hearing the news of his brother's death, Uncle Tony started screaming and crying, "Giovanni is dead!" and he bolted from the house. His befuddled family didn't know where he went or what he did. He simply disappeared.

Everyone who was anyone in our town used the Moroccan Funeral Home, a huge converted mansion designed with the gaudy in mind. The Moroccan theme transported the mourners to a land beyond death and beyond New Jersey suffering. Death became a surreal experience of possibilities, even to the vision of the deceased riding a flying carpet to Heaven. It could have happened. Hidden in the heavy green and gold drapes layered with enormous gold tassels were speakers sending out mood music to enhance the event. And events they were.

As kids, we would escape from our parent's wadded-up-tissue grasps to explore down the wide carpeted stairways that led to the basement "slab" rooms. We had heard tales of IVs stuck in the arms of the dead with blood being drained out. We wanted to see the stiffs on the slabs, their throats and wrists slit, and the blood dripping into buckets. Like hell we did. We would clump together in a group and whisper from locked door to locked door hoping the knob wouldn't turn. They never did, thank heavens.

On the third and final night of Giovanni's wake, everyone was screaming and carrying on, and Mom and I were giving out Oscar nominations when Uncle Tony burst through the swinging rear doors yelling, "Giovanni, Giovanniiiiiiiii, my brother, is dead!" All grieving was put on hold and we stared in disbelief as Uncle Tony lunged and screamed his way up the aisle to the coffin.

God knows Uncle Tony's route to the Moroccan Funeral Home. He had left two days before and had probably ridden 14 trains, 6 buses, and no telling how many thumbed-down cars to get there. The smell emanating from him was putrid, especially mixed with the rotting flowers of the bleeding hearts and gladioli sprays.

Everyone began screaming, their arms outstretched as if they had seen a vision because they didn't know if he was going to be found dead, too. The mourners parted as he stumbled up the aisle and fell onto the open coffin. Even those exhausted from mourning began sobbing at the sight of the two unreconciled brothers finally united by death. Uncle Tony was wailing, "Giovanni, Dio mio!"

In his hysteria he grabbed at my grandfather and suddenly lifted him out of the coffin. Granddad's head went back and that signaled the start of bloodcurdling stereo screams from every point in the room. The noise was deafening.

Have you ever seen a stiff being lifted out of a coffin? It looked like Frankenstein lifting the Bride of Frankenstein out of the box for a dance.

My grandmother began ringing her hands and yelling, "Pleeeeeease put him back, please put him back. Giovanni will have no rest."

The two lurched toward my grandmother, and she gave way to the floor in a dead faint. Others scattered, sending the velvet-covered folding chairs clattering into tangled heaps as the supple and the stiff approached.

The funeral director strode into the fray clapping his soft, white hands, signaling for help from his boys. Mom and I looked at each other and did a check. This definitely would win the Oscar for this funeral, no doubt about it, not even close.

The mourners were evacuated so that the body could be repositioned and smelling salts administered. From that day on when a Somertino died, the family was not allowed to have a fully opened coffin, only a half-opened one at best. No one wanted to take a chance on messing up another deceased's eternal rest.

18

WEDDINGS

I WAS IN MY MID-TEENS WHEN I AUDITIONED FOR AND GOT THE
starring role of Riff, the leader of the Jets, in a touring company
of *West Side Story*. We were on tour when the family wedding-
epidemic began. For several years it seemed as though we were
attending a wedding a month, although in reality it was probably
fewer than that. These episodes are known as the wedding
stories.

The sheer number of weddings occurring during a three-
year span was staggering, and each bride reached into the deepest
recesses of her brain to mastermind the most clever, beautiful,
and original wedding imaginable. Never let it be said that the
Somertinos were boring.

One wedding ceremony was capped off with the premature
release of hundreds of white balloons that rose to the church's
ceiling, only to be spiked by the crystal chandeliers. The final
vows and recessional were interrupted by explosive pops and
dull splats of the spent, limp rubber raining down from on
high. A little bit like condom confetti.

Another wedding's finale included the release of scores of
doves that circled menacingly over the wedding party gathered

on the church steps, and soon a shower began when they relieved their pent-up bladders onto the party with pinpoint accuracy. Forget rice or birdseed, our family put an original twist into every wedding. One poor cousin chose to end her wedding rising up in a gondola balloon. Therefore, each wedding was an event not to be missed for any reason.

Darlene, or Hefty Hannah, as she was known to us second cousins, was one of the first to marry. Even though she weighed in at about 300-plus pounds, she envisioned herself as the southern-belle type and chose an enormous, princess-style bridal gown. The multi-leveled hoopskirt extended the dress to an awe-inspiring ten-foot circle. And powerful hoops they were. When one edge of the dress pressed into a chair or person, the opposite edge would fly up in the air, exposing enormous, pale legs encapsulated in those hard-to-get "plus"-sized stockings. At those moments, onlookers were exposed to a brief glimpse of Darlene's puffy feet that looked like warm dough rising out of a pan. With some practice, she thought she had conquered the nuances of gown control and began her wedding with the confidence only a bride can know.

The Grand Walk began and all guests slowly turned to the rear of the church. We squinted because of the glare from a white wall of fabric bumping every pew as it made its way up the aisle, and we also squinted because our eyes were confused. Darlene's frail father looked like a tuxedo-clad puppet on her enormous arm. At 5'2", poor Uncle Sam was almost invisible. He was edged into every pew as they squeezed themselves and the dress down the impossibly narrow aisle. About halfway to the altar, Darlene began to tilt, list, and finally, sink. Her feet became entangled in the satin trailer covering the carpet, and the bridal titanic resoundingly hit the floor carrying her puppet father with her.

The wedding guests behind them saw a mass of tangled satin and lace. Those in front saw much more when the hoops did their job, elevating the tent over Darlene's head. The little marionette father of the bride attended to his fallen daughter, somehow righted the disaster, and the wedding went on.

19

BENNY

FROM *GONE WITH THE WIND* TO SU CASA. THE NEXT WEDDING reception was held at the Su Casa Hall, chosen for its theatrical winding stairway. Cousin Anna had always dreamed of being presented to adoring masses from the top of this beautiful staircase just like Cinderella with her Prince at the big Ball.

Shortly after their wedding, Anna and her prince, Charles, peeked down at the wedding party below them. The guests mingled, clinked celebratory toasts to the bride and groom, and quietly waited with great anticipation for their arrival at the top of the staircase. The dance band performed its warm-up numbers at half volume. Oh, the anticipation. Everyone checked the top banister occasionally for the arrival of trumpeter Benny O'Malley. Benny, a 4'11" dwarf, had announced the arrival of hundreds of new couples throughout his illustrious, 20-year trumpeting career at Su Casa. The guests with a long-time Casa association knew what to look for—a shiny, long trumpet bell protruding between the rails of the banister.

When the crowd saw its bronze appearance, instant quiet fell over the hall. With one purposeful step, Benny slid between the carved wooden rails, beamed an elfish grin at his audience, and drew a deep, theatrical breath. Oh, how he relished the power he held over the party. With his sequined bolero jacket sparkling as it expanded, he filled his lungs with enough air to properly announce Mr. and Mrs. Charles Haggenborough. Goosebumps popped up on all exposed skin around the room as his ear-splitting number hypnotized (and deafened) the party.

At the end of his flawless performance, the bride and groom appeared on the landing three stories up. Spotlights circled crazily and finally locked onto the smiling, waving couple. A deep bass voice of a Don Pardo wannabe boomed out, "And now, Ladies and Gentlemen, may I introduce to you, Mr. and Mrs. Charles Haggenborough." The couple bowed to the wild cheering and applause from the guests below, and then began the slow descent.

At least the first part was slow. Unfortunately, the bride became tangled in her dress. Somewhere near the top of the stairs, Anna's high heel caught in her slip, and she tumbled forward. Charles felt a jerk on his arm that was linked with hers and was unable to stop the momentum or free himself from impending disaster. Down, down they rolled, looking like—well, imagine the view inside a blender making a bizarre puree with a Bridal Barbie and Ken doll.

Everyone followed each flip and thud with unified gasps of horror. The slow-motion disaster took time to play out as the bride and groom somersaulted down the three flights of 360-degree curved stairs.

At long last, the two lay in a heap on the bottom landing. The band had stopped, Benny ran to help, and the hushed crowd closed in to survey the damage. Great moans surfaced from deep within the white satin mountain. Poor Anna had to be carried away in an ambulance instead of a limousine. Her broken leg healed, but down through the years she steadfastly refused to read the Cinderella story to her kids. Just too many bad memories.

20

LUCILLE

THE FUNNIEST FAMILY WEDDING OCCURRED ON A SWELTERING afternoon on Staten Island. The church was packed with half of Italy, including long-lost aunts and cousins who gathered to support Uncle Vinny at his second marriage. Lucille, his first wife, had passed away of cancer two years before, and he had really snagged a lovely new bride-to-be, Evelyn. Everyone was thrilled for him, except for some of the superstitious old aunts who wondered, "What would Lucille think?"

Aunt Kate and Aunt Rose sat all puffed up, their warts practically standing at attention. I could hear the deceased's name being whispered between them, "Lucille...what would Lucille think?"

We sweated in our formal clothes, patiently contemplating the sacred ceremony that was about to happen, when the organ music announced the bride. Evelyn was radiant as she walked up the aisle. Simultaneously, a scrawny, spotted dog with a torn ear eased open the front door of the church and ran past the bride towards the altar. He bounded by the surprised Evelyn and headed straight to the floral arrangements, where he sniffed and then pissed on them before he barked and growled at the priest. The altar boy lunged for him, but the dog ran back down the aisle and out of the church. We sat stunned. The aunts exchanged knowing glances, like people who have some inside information. They were mouthing, "Lucille" to each other. Their eyes were dilated, their eyebrows on alert.

Just before the electrical storm began, we could hear Uncle Vinny coughing like he had black lung disease. He wasn't ill, just a nervous wreck. Several close lightening strikes shook the walls and caused the aunts' painted-on eyebrows to rise again.

"Lucille," they whispered knowingly.

Between thundering claps that muted the priest's words, we heard the frantic dog scratching at the door. The barking animal made his second appearance and ran towards the altar again to the delight of the superstitious aunts. He circled the priest and bride, and hiked his hind leg to mark the groom's trousers before the altar boy could grab him and deposit the unwelcome intruder back outside into the storm.

"Lucille," they whispered.

The atmosphere was electric with superstitions by now. Aunt Kate and Aunt Rose gathered support from the other old aunts and cousins. Lucille's name bounced like a pinball from pew to pew but the priest moved along with the ceremony as best he could. He turned to the bride and she vowed to cherish and obey her new husband with a pleasant, "I do." He looked at my Uncle Vinny, and read the same passages. But Uncle Vinny began choking and couldn't say a word. His poor narrow shoulders shook, his face became crimson, and he couldn't stop coughing.

"Lucille...Lucille's definitely here," confirmed the old ones. The old wrinkled faces turned and nodded toward one another, their tightly wound hair-buns moved in unison.

A wedding simply can't skip the groom's response and just hop on over it to the kiss and reception, so we waited and waited. We were so embarrassed for him, and I stood transfixed as the coughing spell continued for what seemed like ten minutes. Finally, I rushed to the water fountain and brought him some water which allowed him to cough out, "I do."

The rest of the wedding was conducted with the stereo sounds of Uncle Vinny's coughing, cracking thunder, frantic dog scratches on the church doors, and the not-so-muted whisperings of "Lucille...Lucille..."

Much to the old aunts' dismay, the wedding party emerged outside after the ceremony to a glorious, sunny day. The dog had gone and Lucille had ridden the clouds to her eternal rest, satisfied in knowing that her dear Vinny and Evelyn had passed her tests with flying colors.

21

TRAIN

AFTER SO MANY WEDDING DISASTERS, INCLUDING PIGEON-SHIT, gondolas gone mad, midgets with trumpets, stairways to hell, pissing dogs, ghosts from the grave, and one cousin Cara who wore enough chiffon to mummify the Statue of Liberty, our family was about to require that all the Somertino children become priests or nuns just to avoid continued embarrassments. But, true to the law of averages, the family's luck finally changed. Karen, my most beautiful and dearest cousin, became the next bride-to-be.

Surprisingly, Karen's wedding went without a hitch. She remembered her family's wedding heritage and was determined not to repeat the disasters, especially not the chiffon disaster that threw the bride to the floor when she tried to turn to the Blessed Virgin and the yards of chiffon ate her alive.

The flowers had arrived on time, Karen's hair and makeup were perfect, the church was breathtakingly beautiful with scores of lighted candles, and everyone was seated and ready for the ceremony exactly on time.

One rather major omission was discussed among the old aunts, however. The white satin cloth that was supposed to be placed in the aisle from the back of the church to the altar was missing. This caused great concern among the superstitious aunts. They discussed the problem and passed their thoughts up and down the pews until the organ music signaled the Grand Walk.

Karen looked gorgeous, like Audrey Hepburn in *My Fair Lady*. Her off-the-shoulder gown was stunningly beautiful. The white taffeta-and-lace dress was a showstopper. The audience absorbed her elegant beauty as she moved down the aisle and gradually they became aware of her wedding train. The satin-and-lace train had no end. As Karen advanced to the altar, the stiff train extended on and on and on and out the door of the church.

People couldn't believe it. No one had ever seen a wedding train so beautiful or long. It electrified the stunned onlookers and caused the further distracting thoughts of "How is she going to turn and exit the church?" This question completely captivated the group and monopolized their thoughts to the extent that no one even heard the vows.

At the end of the ceremony, Karen slowly kissed Bill and then with one deft motion she unhooked the train and it slid to the floor. Turning, she stepped onto what was now a beautiful white runner, and, with her groom at her side, she exited the church to a standing ovation. The guests jumped to their feet and began cheering wildly—finally, our family's luck had changed.

22

MEETING

BETWEEN THE NUMEROUS FAMILY WEDDINGS, I CONTINUED WITH the touring company of *West Side Story*. This experience of playing Riff, the leader of the Jets, was far more exciting than I expected and we played to appreciative audiences all across the United States. The six-month tour closed out in Los Angeles where for several performances there had been a buzz backstage about a famous Hollywood star being in the audience. Brik Moor, the most popular television and movie star of the 1970s and early 1980s had attended seven or eight of our nightly performances and that had created quite a stir with the cast and crew.

Night after night, Brik beamed his handsome smile from his prime seat in the audience. I remember noticing him as I moved across the stage. Even through the glare of floodlights at my feet, his presence could be seen and felt. He had chosen a seat near the center of the stage and within the flare of reflected stage light. It was flattering to observe his reaction to my performance. At that point, however, I assumed he was flashing his million-dollar smile at everyone.

To be a young performer involved in a well-accepted, sold-out show in Los Angeles meant feeling euphorically optimistic. I was fulfilling my destiny; I was born to perform. Everywhere I turned, people were complimenting me and seeking me out as a companion. Needless to say, I was filled with confidence and purpose and could hardly wait for my next acting challenges. Absolutely everything was going my way at the time, with wonderful reviews of *West Side Story* and the flush of a successful Hollywood career almost upon me.

With one week remaining of *West Side Story*, we were to celebrate our successes and the conclusion of the tour at the Mediterranean-style estate of Jason Litch. The entire cast was invited to a lavish party at the Litchs' sprawling estate on Bel Air Drive, near Beverly Hills. That evening several limousines were dispatched to our hotel to bring us to the party, and we were groomed to within an inch of our lives. I had ridden in a limousine before, but never to such an opulent house, and certainly never for such an occasion. I later discovered it was an occasion orchestrated by Brik. The party was to honor the cast, or so we thought. Actually, it had been planned by Brik and Jason Litch as a way for Brik to meet me.

Our limousine cruised past the uniformed security guard and electronic gate up the inclined driveway to the waiting doorman standing at the front curb. As I stepped from the back of the limo, I glanced about and was enthralled at the view of the city lights extending for miles in the valley below. It felt as if we were at a castle on the highest hill looking down on all the unfortunate, underprivileged people. Music and soft yellow light flooded out of the enormous windows. The air was electric.

To be honest, I was impressed but not overwhelmed by the affair. Servants balanced silver trays loaded with caviar and champagne. An empty hand was quickly filled with whatever the guest desired. A wonderful six-piece band played inspired music that bathed over the guests standing about in small clusters chatting softly and laughing occasionally.

Actually, I felt right at home in this environment. I had always fantasized about being a star in Beverly Hills, even as a boy in New Jersey, and for years I had mentally prepared myself for this reality. Above the party on the second level were small balconies with ornate, white wrought-iron railings and lush leafy plants that softened the stuccoed walls. Enormous, brightly colored canvases entertained the eyes of those who were between conversations. But I wasn't there to be entertained, and I was never between conversations.

At one point I had a group of friends ringed around me as I launched into a story about some person who had been in the audience that night and had come backstage. I was in my element, complete with exact dialogue and animated gestures. My friends were greatly absorbed in the story, listening intently, when I felt a tap on my shoulder. It was Brik.

I stopped mid-sentence, whirled around to see who was interrupting me, and saw a very handsome man holding two glasses of champagne. My first comment to this established movie and television star was, "Can't you see I'm busy? You'll have to wait."

"I want to talk with you," he smiled.

"Well, let me finish my story with my friends, then I'll meet you." Then I asked, "What's that in your hand?"

"I thought you'd enjoy a glass of champagne," replied Brik.

"What's wrong with you? I'm not of legal age to drink." I looked at him with very suspicious eyes.

After some time and several more stories, I walked over to the glass French doors that were swung open to expose a view of the terraced gardens and city below. Translucent white curtains were drawn out of the party and into the night by the warm summer breeze.

Waiting alone on the first terrace was Brik. He certainly was handsome—blond hair, tall physique, squared shoulders, and a smile that could light up a room—but I was not bowled over by him. Nor was I that familiar with his movies and television shows. I had been so wrapped up in my own career, I really wasn't that impressed with his.

I walked across the Belgian block terrace edged with great stone pillars and a European-style brick wall to meet this handsome star. We began our first conversation with a stroll through the manicured gardens that surrounded the estate.

Brik turned to me and said, "I'm very interested in your career. You know, you're quite a talent."

I don't remember exactly what else was said that evening, but I was a bit puzzled by his interest. He wanted to have lunch or dinner with me before the tour ended and we returned to New York. I said, "Sure, give me a call."

The party ended; we were loaded into the limo and swept away back to our hotel. I tapped my fingers on the leather armrest as I glanced out the tinted windows and watched the expansive mansions flicker by. The evening had been wonderful yet mysterious, too.

He did call for dinner and he even sent chocolates and flowers to my room, but I never returned his phone calls. The girls in the cast were flabbergasted by his interest in me and my cavalier attitude towards him, but I was too busy having fun and really didn't want to be bothered. So, without speaking with him again, I returned home when the show ended.

23

MODEL

SEVERAL MONTHS PASSED AND I WAS BACK IN NEW YORK CITY continuing my modeling career with Lord and Taylor. Others might have viewed my job with awed interest, but to me it was just a job. Modeling had been a continuing part of my life since early childhood, like baseball or soccer is for other children. I grew quite accustomed to the routine of being a runway model.

In a bare, ceiling-less staging area each model had a tiny staked-out space. Mirrors reflected perfection and the manic commotion of the events. "Uncontrolled chaos" best describes the backstage scene. The models were treated like queen bees with countless workers' hands adjusting, tucking in, slicking down, and fluffing up the objects of their concentration.

The dressing area was awash with layers of smoke and the sounds of clothing racks squeaking on the cement floor. Cluttered all about were small open cases, jammed and spilling over with essentials like hair spray, makeup, and casual clothes to wear home. Observers would hear conversational bursts that only contained the essentials—"under the black pants," "too loose," "shit."

There is no such thing as "personal space" in the model's vocabulary and modesty was shed at the door. Dressers with purposeful, concentrated stares would home in on the models' hems, belts, sleeves, boobs, and butts. They had some vision of how best to express the look of the ensemble and, by God, that was the look they would achieve.

Runway models would evolve into something inhuman as the tensions rose, and screeches of "Bitch!" and "Fucking bitch!" peppered the air as the dressers squeezed, gouged, and pinned the hell out of some poor, thin victim.

After striding off the runway, I would undo zippers and buttons, and, with a patented kicking motion, launch the spent garments into a carcass pile for some unfortunate soul to hang up.

Out of the corner of my eye, I could see an approaching attack of the dresser bearing down on me with my next outfit in tow. Common characteristics among the dressers were the straight-pin dentures that stuck to their lips and moved ever so slightly as they grimaced out commands. As I quickly discovered, these pins were their tools of behavior modification.

I tried my best to be a compliant model after suffering a slight accident midway during a show one day. My foot ripped the back seam of some pants I was supposed to wear. Armed with a mouthful of straight pins, the dresser quickly wove them into place, and I was ordered on my way with a wave of her hand. Never before had such pain emanated from that area of my body. Every step forced one butt-cheek, then the other, into certain pointed pain. I shuffled my way to the stage door issuing a stream of well-deserved curse words and looked back to see the damned dresser with a slight, silver smile on her face.

As we readied ourselves with our next outfit, we had a subconscious awareness of the flow of the show. The sounds of the announcer, the music, and the audience cued us about how much time we had before we were to next appear. The backstage director hovered at the curtain's entrance armed with a walkie-talkie and frantically waved as she tried to achieve the scripted order of show.

We would cluster at the door in the order of our appearance, just seconds before we were to walk the runway. With clock-like precision, the director would pop her Wrigley's gum in my ear and shove me out like a drill sergeant with her paratroopers. For a few applause-filled moments, I would feel superhuman. It was thrilling to be appreciated at one's peak of perfection. With my stride timed to the musical score, I strutted down the runway and swallowed people up with a piercing smile. This routine would be repeated many times before the night was through.

One rainy October night I left the service entrance of Lord and Taylor with my duffel bag and my collar turned up to protect my neck from the biting wind. I was only a few steps out the door when I was confronted by a man holding a large black umbrella. He tipped the umbrella to allow reflected street lights to reveal his identity. It was Brik.

"It's storming and I thought you might want a ride home," he yelled. In a surprised state, I was gathered under his umbrella and whisked away to his limousine. While I was overwhelmed with appreciation of his attention and concern for me, I was slightly puzzled.

It was good to see him again and we enjoyed our conversation on the way home. I had forgotten how handsome he was. Brik told me he wanted to help with my career. It was something of a payback after having gotten his start in Hollywood when a famous star had taken an interest in him. Brik had been brought to Los Angeles, and put in the MGM theatrical school where he was picked to star in a television series. Why would I be suspicious of a true good luck story like that? I might roll the dice with him, I thought.

Even though it was dark when we pulled in my driveway, the curtains parted up and down the street as curious neighbors investigated the arrival of the limousine. Brik and I shook out the umbrella and our coats as we entered my home where Dad was reading the newspaper, my sister was on the phone in the hall, and my mom was working in the kitchen.

My sister turned from her secretive conversation, focused in on Brik, screamed, and dropped the phone as she ran to comb her hair for the famous guest. Dad graciously welcomed this handsome stranger into his home as I approached Mom with a request that he stay for dinner.

Brik, however, suggested that he treat everyone at the local steakhouse where the restaurant staff fell into turmoil over the presence of such a star. Waitresses showered our table with unwanted attention, and the other guests prolonged their meals just to watch the handsome star dine. He spoke to my parents about wanting to help me with my career, and about his connections with the most advantageous people who could help me make it big in Hollywood. He told them that he wanted me to stay with him for the summer, and that he would take me under his wing.

Because of his reputation and sterling qualities, his convincing case persuaded my parents to let me go to Los Angeles to stay with him after school was out and I was handed over to him on a silver platter. At my "going away" party celebrated that June, Mom joked that she had reserved mantle space for my future Oscar.

24

CALIFORNIA

THE FLIGHT FROM NEW JERSEY TO LAX WAS ONE OF WHIRLING
expectations with endless questions that kept looping through
my immature mind. What adventures would this summer hold
for me? Would I meet someone who would help me to stardom?
Would Brik and I get along? Would he be sorry that he had
invited me? Was this a big mistake? Brik met me in baggage
claim with a heart-melting smile, and all my concerns subsided.
I gathered my luggage and tossed it into the back seat of his
Mercedes convertible. Hollywood, here I come.

We headed north toward Malibu with the setting sun
warming our wind-blown hair and the Pacific waves licking at
the shore. I leaned my head back and thanked God for my
many blessings. Brik drove confidently up the coastal highway
and occasionally turned his radiant face toward me to smile a
silent "Welcome to your new home" look toward me. I was
given a bedroom in Brik's home with a wonderful ocean view,
and I quickly settled into a comfortable routine.

Brik was on hiatus from television and between movies, so
we had the luxury of unstructured days to forge a friendship.
After enjoying a small breakfast of a cup of coffee, a bagel, and

fruit on the back deck of his home, we would greet the morning with a run along the beach. Many times I would look out over the ocean and wonder at my good fortune. I quickly adjusted to life with a loving, protective companion who genuinely cared for me and my family, one who eventually stole my heart. I remember having for the first time the deep feelings of love for another human being.

As days turned into weeks, our relationship strengthened into more than just a friendship. We touched each other frequently, leaned into each other when we wanted to share something special. To have Brik's arms wrapped around my shoulders filled me with the warmest feelings of security and love. His kiss was as sweet and delicious as chocolate melting in the warm sun. It was only natural that more physical intimacy would follow the playful courtship of the beginning of our relationship.

Weeks passed and we gradually realized that we wanted a sexual intimacy that neither of us had ever experienced before. Now, Brik was very experienced with women but had never engaged in sexual love with a man (at least as far as I knew). I had been basically sexless until then and was completely unknowledgeable about lovemaking, although I had realized that I liked the company of men.

Brik talked to me about the things women did with men, sexual pleasures, and fantasies. Over time I felt completely captivated by his charm and realized I was hopelessly in love with him. Sexual tension between us increased until we knew the time had come to experiment with sex.

We decided to begin the romantic evening at La Scala, a fine Italian restaurant where Brik and I lifted a glass of wine to celebrate the coming evening. By candlelight we relished the ravioli, chicken parmigiana, chopped salad, and buttery garlic rolls, (looking back, maybe we should have kept it to a chopped salad and a roll of breath mints), but our eyes rarely left each other's as we anticipated the night together.

It was 11:00 p.m. when we arrived home and changed out of our dinner clothes into comfortable shorts and windbreakers. Brik called to me from the back deck. We stepped off the sandy stairs, our feet sank into the warm sand, and hand-in-hand we walked toward the ocean. No words were spoken; none were needed. With the ocean orchestra pounding out its timeless melody, he drew me into his muscular chest and kissed me with a fierceness I had never known. His forceful hold on me filled me with an intense desire for him. We quickly turned and pulled each other back to the house, dropping our clothes with wild abandon along the way.

In one fluid motion Brik pulled me toward him as we ascended the stairs, then gently lifted me into his arms like his most prized possession. I melted into his loving arms, as he kicked open the French door with his foot and carried me to his bed. (Harlequin Romance fans, eat your heart out.)

Let's just put it this way, what happened next wasn't what I had imagined. My initiation into intimacy fell far short of the satisfaction mark as I gagged and vomited.

"Now, see what you made me do? You clean it up!" I wailed as I flew to my room in embarrassment. I threw myself across my bed, completely disappointed in myself and in the evening. The disastrous anticlimax was softened somewhat later that night, when Brik entered my room, lay down beside me and softly stroked and comforted me. Without passion, without sex, without tension, our bodies blended together into a deep, satisfying sleep.

25

BETTE

OUR RELATIONSHIP CONTINUED TO GROW AS THE DAYS TURNED into months, and I began making plans for my future. During the next few years, I enrolled in courses at UCLA and the New York Academy of Dramatic Arts. I had an apartment in New York City where I stayed during the week, and frequently I flew back to Los Angeles for the weekend.

These were heady, carefree years. I was completely devoted to the love of my life, yet had the freedom to pursue my dream of being a star. Brik's attraction to women never interfered with our love for each other. We accepted each other's needs, kept our individuality, and yet built a lasting, intertwined marriage of sorts, with a timeless passion that never diminished.

Some of my favorite memories of these years in New York involve a lifelong friend, Bette—not Midler or Davis—but a star in her own right. We had met as young teenagers at the Helen Merritt Vocal Studio and had laughed ourselves into oblivion more times than I can remember.

Her humor, so self-effacing, earthy, and laser-sharp, could send me into spasms of laughter. Over the years I only remember good times with Bette. Her life took a path off the beat of entertainment celebrity, (where she certainly should have traveled) but she has been influential to another kind of audience as an educator.

We took acting courses together at New York Dramatic Arts College and sought out each other's company at every turn. After classes in the late afternoon we would meet at Cathy's, the local watering hole around the corner from school.

No one seemed to notice the truly survivalistic furnishings at Cathy's or the perpetually smeared windows that were supposed to allow you to look out over the street. Stepping down two chipped linoleum steps into our student "home away from home" became a comfortable habit. Draft beer was a favorite of the college students, and the harried bartender's left hand almost never lost its grip on the keg's wooden handle. Old Harry would tip his head at us as we entered.

Bette and I would meet and entertain each other over the commotion of the crowded room. Whether we were just beginning to knock down a few beers or were winding up the evening, we were the loudest and most intense customers there. We would drag worn-out wooden chairs close together at the table, wrap our hands around a frosty mug, and begin firing stories at one another.

We weren't polite to each another; our friendship was beyond that. Whoever could power their story to the forefront got to be first, with the other layering in approval, disapproval, colorations, and expletives as needed. As manic as it sounds, these interactions became absolutely essential to my life.

One evening, some guys were slamming down dollar bills to pay the tabs, gathering jackets, and leaving for the night. Bette and I were there for the long haul, however, and had branched apart momentarily. I was full of myself as usual and was flirting with anyone who caught my attention. (As good as

I was at flirting, I was loyal to Brik for 24 years, however.) I glanced over my shoulder to see three young men circling Bette and moving in for kisses and hugs. Later I found out they were goading her with propositions and pleading requests to come outside for an alley blowjob.

But from across the room, all I heard was Bette's booming voice yelling out, "What's the matter, doesn't anybody fuck anymore?" Those skinny boys scattered like rabbits in the night and left the stunned patrons with a final laugh for the evening.

Another time Bette and I were really shit-faced and ripe for trouble. She had gathered a horny group of five nasty-mouthed guys around her who began pulling on her and imploring her to go with them to an apartment.

She was willing and wanted to go, but I jerked her aside and said to her, "You don't want to go with them. All they want to do is rip your clothes off, pinch your titties, jerk off, shoot their load in your face, and sodomize you. When they're done, they'll just throw your ass out in the street. You don't want that, do you?"

Her clear eyes zeroed in on mine and said, "Yeeeeeeeeeeeeeeeeeah, I do."

Of course, I wouldn't let her go, but we laughed about that for years. If ever asked the question, "What three people would you want to keep you company on a deserted island?", my answer would include Bette.

26

FRANCESCA

I WAS IN CALIFORNIA WHEN I RECEIVED WORD OF MY SISTER'S upcoming wedding. Francesca and Mom requested my presence to help with the endless wedding plans, so I booked a flight home. Onboard the flight, I reviewed the recent family wedding disasters and swore to avoid the known pitfalls of doves, balloons, gondolas, princess dresses, and stairways. I should have added mantillas to the list.

Francesca was beautiful, and she was then the thinnest of her life. Actually, both she and her fiancé Ted were weighing in at an all-time low. We traipsed about New York looking for gowns and headpieces where finally, at Bergdorf Goodman's, she found the most beautiful gown that enhanced her beauty to that of a movie star. Everything was perfect, except for her headdress.

Mom and I had suggested she choose something to frame her pretty face, like baby's breath woven into her hair, but she stubbornly refused. Instead, she adamantly insisted on wearing a mantilla. We replied thoughtlessly that she would look more like a Puerto Rican stomping down the aisle with castanets in each hand instead of a nice Italian, Catholic girl. Nothing we said dissuaded her in her choice, however. And it was, after all, her wedding.

The morning of the wedding Francesca and I got together over a muffin at the kitchen table. We looked at each other and she burst into tears, saying, "I think I'm the only bride in history to get hit with an ugly stick on the day of her wedding." I had to admit it, she was right. Her hair was curled so tightly she looked like the lion in the *Wizard of Oz* after his makeover. And with just an hour and a half until the wedding, she had no time for a restyling. She mounted the mantilla in place and drove to the church in tears.

I was so proud to escort my beautiful mother down the aisle that day. She stole the show with her lavender lace-and-sequined gown and a luxurious white-fox stole draped around her shoulders. People leaned out into the aisle to compliment her. She whispered softly to me as we began the long walk, "Tony, take this slow. We only do this once." During the five minutes it took me to get her seated, we missed the commotion going on in the vestibule of the church.

My grandmother, Arcangela, had arrived slightly late and had reacted to the emotional moment by grabbing Francesca. Both were hugging, kissing, and crying convulsively. Francesca's mascara advanced down her cheeks and gave her that ever so popular coal miner's look. In her exuberance, Arcangela pulled Francesca's mantilla completely off her head and she was whisked away to her seat in the front of the church leaving Francesca to repair the mess. My dad tried to right the contraption but only succeeded in loosely reattaching it near her ear when the Wedding March began and the doors were flung open.

From our vantage point near the altar, Mom and I could see a beautiful dress coming slowly down the aisle, but we were in a state of shock to discover that it was being worn by an Alice Cooper apparition. Neither of us had good eyesight anyway so we just exchanged puzzled looks and then stared down the aisle as my sister and my dad approached. Mom turned to me and said, "Who's that?"

I said, "I have no idea."

It was like a before and after Halloween makeover. Her eyes were swollen shut, black channels of mascara trailed down her cheeks, and her coiffure had imploded. As Francesca reached our seats, she turned to look at me, and I whispered to her, "What the fuck happened to you?"

She whimpered, "Grandma got me at the back of the church."

"Oh, Francesca..."

"Don't even say. The pictures will tell it all."

And they did. The photographer, not wanting to put out a poor product, painted Francesca's eyes onto her puffy, closed eyelids. Great. The result is a permanent record of a demented looking bride with eyes of varying sizes protruding from smeared war paint. Congratulations, dear.

27

ROCK

EARLY HOLLYWOOD WAS MAGIC AND ILLUSION. "THAT'S WHAT keeps them coming back"—that was what the audience paid for at the box office. Before the 1970s, very little unfavorable information about the lives of Hollywood stars was leaked through their privacy fences. The public received only contrived, well-edited information about these Hollywood legends through the publicists and well-paid agents whose oversized egos fantasized that they had molded lives and created personas the public would pay to see. In a way, they were right.

Need a blond? Here's the bleach. Got to have an aging, mature, heavyset woman? Here, Rosemary, have another chocolate. How about a Brooklyn gang member or a southern belle? Spend a few months with the "natives" and absorb the ambiance; eat the bratwurst or collard greens; talk the talk and walk the walk. Why do people pay to escape momentarily into another life? Because it is fascinating to experience the freedom of being someone else without reaping the repercussions of that lifestyle. In the most convincing movies, the audience is transported away for a couple of hours to exotic locations, dangerous environments, or forbidden personal situations. For many, these experiences are more memorable than their real lives. Some people remember being so affected by a film that upon leaving the theater, they feel jarred by reality, and in some instances the movie continues on in their minds long after leaving the show.

That is the fantasy; that is the magic. The observers didn't have to break out of a burning high-rise building or have their legs cut off with a rusty scout knife after an intense mortar attack or get knocked up with their father's half-witted baby or grub for dirty potatoes in a field scorched by General Sherman. Popcorn kernels stuck between the teeth can be the only down side of movie going.

During the years I lived in Beverly Hills, I was given a peek behind the stage curtain. I sometimes wish I'd never looked. Take Rock Hudson, for instance.

I was forewarned before going to his estate for his traditional Sunday afternoon pool party that the "real" Rock Hudson was extremely different from his public persona. The entire time we were driving to his house, I prepared myself for the most extreme character my imagination could muster, and that's not to be taken lightly because I have a great imagination and had just about seen it all by this time.

Our driver whisked us through the gates of an expansive Spanish-style mansion fit for the star that Rock was. Through the tinted backseat windows, I saw an unforgettable sight, a 6' 4" Rock Hudson lounging against a two-story pillar at his front entrance. His tan body was wrapped in a paisley caftan, and dangling from those sensuous lips (lusted after by women everywhere) was what seemed to be a foot-long cigarette holder tipped at a jaunty angle. It was a pose from the 1920s. That was Rock Hudson?

Stunned, I could not slide out of the car when it rolled to a stop until Rock's greeting jarred my senses: "Come on in, girls. We're having a ball!"

Brik watched my expressions eagerly and apparently was well rewarded for his vigilance. I was totally dazed and had to sit down to collect myself when we walked around the back of the house to the pool. Even though I'd been warned, I must admit that my finely tuned imagination fell far short of the creative mark when it came to predicting Rock's personality.

He moved with a self-assured grace and was silly. Silly? Yes, and fun. I couldn't keep my eyes off him the entire afternoon. The mysterious transformation from the masculine, handsome leading man, to an engaging host with a wicked sense of earthy humor was fascinating, to say the least. I kept handing him out imaginary Oscars and Emmys as the afternoon progressed.

The studios could never have marketed the Rock Hudson I saw that day. What they needed was an unattainable, incredibly handsome guy for Doris Day to pursue for three light-hearted movies, and that's what he gave them.

Of course, women loved him. He looked like every man would choose to look, and his lively dark eyes reflected humor and restraint. He wasn't a sensual animal who would lay out a woman on the kitchen table like Jack Nicholson did to Jessica Lange. He was a safer fantasy for women. After all, if Doris Day couldn't quite get her legs wrapped around him, then who could?

But women love a chase and to cuddle up to someone who reminds them of the son they wish they'd had. This incredibly gifted actor gave the public exactly what they wanted just as Marilyn Monroe had done. (Do you think the Kennedys would have wanted to rub up against a "Norma Jean"?) Theirs was a skill, a gift, a true talent.

In the end, when Rock languished with AIDS, his friends protected his privacy and his secrets. His adoring public was unaware of his sexuality and his disease until the very end. Elizabeth Taylor and others rallied around the Rock Hudson they knew and loved, not the movie star Rock Hudson. As he slipped away, his legacy became much greater than a handful of movies or the starring roles in countless women's dreams. He became a rallying point for social acceptability in acknowledging AIDS as a pervasive problem in our society. In my eyes, that was his Oscar; that was his Emmy.

28

TREE

EVENTUALLY SCHOOL WAS OUT IN NEW YORK AND LA, AND I returned to Malibu in time to celebrate my 19th birthday, complete with the car of my dreams...an eye-catching, yellow Corvette. We were just one glowing blur on Highway #1, where the thrill of speeding along the tortuous curves bordering the Pacific Ocean never lessened. Our Malibu home was rather distant from the social hub of Beverly Hills and Hollywood, however, and much of the time I felt detached, and I began to wish for a life in town.

Brik became totally immersed in new television projects that kept him on the set for long hours most days and he understood my loneliness and feelings of detachment. He surprised me one day shortly after my 19th birthday by telling me that we would be moving to Beverly Hills. Suddenly I had a project to sink all of my youthful energies into—my own home.

Our sprawling ranch-style house on Mountain Drive became the backdrop for many adventures and misadventures. With my volatile personality and Brik's willful, quick temperament conflicting occasionally, we created quite a comic relief in the formerly rather subdued neighborhood that included a famous member of the "Rat Pack," and "the" plastic surgeon of the stars.

To personalize and update our new house, I began gathering decorating ideas by seeking out everything that could demonstrate that I knew the meaning of graceful living. I pored through *Better Homes and Gardens* and logged countless hours memorizing my household favorites at the finest stores in Beverly Hills.

With the ability to get whatever it took to achieve cultural nirvana, I began greeting the many deliverymen who brought it right to our door. We wanted the best, and the best to us was the Claire pattern of Waterford crystal, Wallace's Grand Baroque sterling silver, and Carlyle china by Royal Doulton. I deeply desired to know about the refinements of living and entertaining and began educating myself by reading and observing others who had achieved a classy, opulent lifestyle.

I threw myself into broadening my horizons which included every domestic skill from cooking to decorating to fashion to landscaping. Even though he was ten years older than I, Brik was learning, too, and he seemed enthralled by my curious, intense efforts at self-improvement. He was financially and emotionally supportive and encouraging at every Martha Stewart turn.

Perhaps one turn too many....One morning at breakfast I excitedly shoved a deal of a lifetime under Brik's nose. I had just found the perfect solution to our landscaping dilemma: what decorative tree would be perfect in the corner of our newly landscaped courtyard? Unbelievably, we had a once-in-a-lifetime chance to buy—for only $250—a rare double cherry, weeping willow tree from Japan. According to the magazine article, time was short and quantities were limited, our window of opportunity very narrow. "Order today," it demanded. "Be the envy of your family and friends." With a wave of his hand Brik okayed the purchase, and I fired off a check in the morning mail.

Months went by and the double cherry, weeping willow tree from Japan lapsed into a forgotten whim. One Saturday morning Brik busily prepared for his all-important golf game when he was interrupted by the doorbell. Before he could sign his name on the receipt, he glanced past the delivery guy to the street where there was an enormous flatbed truck billowing black smoke as it idled in front of our house. The engine noise and vibration brought anxious neighbors out of their houses gripping their morning coffee. Tony and Brik were at it again.

From the kitchen I heard the door slam and Brik yell, "What the fuck is this?" I came sliding around the corner to see what was wrong. "Your tree is here. And wait until you see the size of it. Plant it. Stick it up your ass. Or do whatever you want with it. I don't care, but I'm going to play golf and I don't want any part of it."

I said, "How big could a tree be for $250?"

A little smaller than a Sequoia.

I was left in charge of this thing and walked out front to see traffic blocked on both sides of the street by a huge flatbed truck with its cargo: an enormous horizontal tree. Surely there had been some mix-up and we had received a $2,500 double cherry, weeping willow Japanese tree instead of a $250 one. I felt inclined to try to get rid of it except that my superstitious nature kept whispering, "No, Tony, remember? You planned for it to go in the corner of the courtyard. There's a reason for everything."

I called for a crane. Another first. There had never been a crane in the neighborhood before, and now the neighbors clustered together to enjoy the spectacle, complete with sandwiches, martinis, and lawn chairs. My heart raced as I marched back and forth and motioned helplessly beside the crane as it lifted the tree over the garage into a hole in the courtyard it had previously dug. Creaking chains swayed the airborne giant into place and I weakly sighed a prayer of thanks. By late afternoon, the place looked pretty much back to normal and the audience had dispersed. Thank God, the show was over.

There was just one big problem; the tree was not the envy of family and friends as promised. From the road, it looked like an enormous tree growing out of the center of our house. From the back yard, well, it *was* the backyard. To maneuver from one end of the yard to the other meant a series of body contortions, which included side straddling, ducking, and parting the leafy willow branches. The proportions were like a real tree in a dollhouse. But I had to act like it was wonderful.

When Brik came home I said, "Isn't it beautiful?"

He replied hotly, "Listen, I'm going to tell you one thing: this whole ordeal has cost a fortune. If that tree dies, so do you."

"That tree won't die. Why should it die? We have a Japanese tree and a Japanese gardener. If needed, I'll give it some sushi; it should be fine."

Two or three months went by when I noticed dead willow leaves lying about the yard. My life flashed before my eyes. The Japanese gardener drove another nail in my coffin by saying, "Oh, Tony, tree no live here. Tree die for sure. Not Japan. No have climate like Japan. No have humidity. Tree die."

"What? Look Wong, tree can't die. We have to do whatever we can to save it."

As soon as Brik left every morning, we would baby it, inject it, fertilize it, but it continued dropping buds, blooms, and leaves without mercy. I wrote my will. A brilliant plan came to me in a moment of despair and I gathered Aunt Bea and Charles, our house staff, to help me save my ass. We bought sacks full of silk leaves, blossoms, and buds and dragged ladders to the dying tree.

Honestly, for hours each day we glued, scotch-taped, and glue-gunned our way into a frenzy of tree rehabilitation. Over time, it became a magnificent dual personality, a unique hybrid specimen. From the road (which apparently Brik never noticed) it looked like a dead, beetle-destroyed bunch of limbs erupting out of the house. From the courtyard, it was a horticulturist's dream, forever blooming and perpetually green.

Some months later, I served our favorite brunch, eggs benedict, on our finest china under our schizophrenic tree. Before we could begin, however, a leaf with a huge piece of Scotch tape on it fell off the tree and into Brik's dish. He looked at me, and I started to cry: "You know what, I'm fucking dead. Kill me already. I'm so tired of going up there."

"Going up there? How long has this thing been dead?"

"About six months. Aunt Bea and Charles and I get on it every day."

He started laughing his ass off. I figured that as long as he was laughing I wasn't dead, so, like Lucille Ball, I laughed along with him and pointed out our handiwork with pride.

"Look, Tony, I appreciate that you tried to save the tree, but the truth is it has been a damned eyesore ever since it was planted. All I ask is that you get it out of here when I'm not here. Not on a Saturday."

The crane, flatbed truck, and workers arrived Saturday morning. Not a good sign. It was like playing a video in reverse, only this time the neighbors were in for extra drama and a surprise ending.

The straining chains finally uprooted the dead tree, and a delighted, hooting crowd was treated to a biologic specimen suitable for "Ripley's Believe it or Not" museum. It's one thing to fuck up secretly, but to publicly screw up like this was a humiliating nightmare. The crane began swinging the poor thing over the house. Every onlooker's head was tilted to get a perfect view. Their curious attention was rewarded when a chain broke and the tree speared through the garage roof and into Brik's new blue Mercedes. Their mouths open and their eyes wide with surprise, the neighbors found themselves in on the ordeal.

Brik lunged for me and began chasing me around the front yard. I was screaming and begging for mercy. He piled into me and brought me down with a forceful tackle and we rolled over and over, emitting inhuman sounds. Even the goading neighbors became concerned and started pulling for me. "Don't choke him! Please don't kill him," they pleaded.

On about the 20th flip and roll, we collapsed into a snorting, laughing pile. He said, "You know, living with you is like being with Lucy and Gracie Allen all rolled up into one!"

29

CHANDELIER

BRIK AND I SETTLED INTO A COMFORTABLE RELATIONSHIP ON
Mountain Drive and I continued making purchases for the house
with his blessings. Gradually everything was falling into place,
except in the relatively plain expansive dining room. Although
it had a beautiful mahogany table and enough chairs to seat
eighteen, as well as an elegant glass wall overlooking the
courtyard, something was missing, and I decided that something
was a chandelier.

Once I became aware of this glaring deficiency, I could
think of nothing else. Oh, the shame of it, an Italian with no
chandelier in the dining room. How crude, how bare, how
unacceptable. Through daily crusades and inquiries I discovered
that the chandelier of excellence (and certainly the one for us)
was a magnificent, sparkling masterpiece made of Waterford
crystal.

"Fine, order it. But don't ever try to clean it. Understand?"
barked Brik.

I agreed readily but without quite understanding the gravity
of his request; anyway, I ordered the $8,000 extravaganza. A
small army of workmen reinforced the ceiling above the dining

room table and hung our new "Maria Teresa" chandelier. I'll admit, the thing was too large for our dining room, too large for any dining room really, except maybe Buckingham Palace.

After the workmen left, I pretended to be preparing for a fancy party and casually walked into the darkened dining room, flipping the switch as I breezed through the doorway. I almost fell to the ground from the blinding sparkles of its intensity. Sunglasses, where are my sunglasses? I ran from the room and called an electrician to install a dimmer on the switch. That solved the problem. When turned to its lowest point, there was a certain comfortable level of glare. People's pupils no longer looked like microscopic dots, and I settled into planning entertainment events that would play out under the chandelier's massive crystal wingspan.

Six months later I ventured into the dining room to prepare for a small dinner party to celebrate a friend's birthday. Hmmm...too dark...I actually reached for the dimmer switch and gave it a turn. While working on a table arrangement, I glanced up into the chandelier and was horrified to see that every crystal wore a milky, hazy, fuzzy coating. I ran to the phone and called my mom in New Jersey for help.

"Oh, Tony, it's very easy. You take the prisms off, soak them in a little ammonia and water. Take them out, dry them, hang them back up, and they'll shine like diamonds," she reassured.

How hard could that be, I thought? When Brik left for the studio one morning, I began the job of cleaning the chandelier. Piece of cake.

I filled a tub with soapy water and ammonia and got to work dismantling the chandelier. Each of the scores of prisms came off easily. Some resembled long dangling earrings, some strings of beaded necklaces, some heart-shaped crystals, and countless others were heavy, clear jewels on a hook.

By mid-morning, I had soft towels lying across every flat surface in the kitchen covered with a Waterford wonderland of clean prisms. Aunt Bea walked through the kitchen at one point and asked me, "Tony, I've just got to ask you one question, do you remember where each one goes where?"

I said, "Well, wherever they fit."

"You're a dead man."

"What's the matter?"

"They fit every hole."

"You have got to be kidding!"

"Is there any kind of diagram?"

"Not that I know of."

Aunt Bea flew out of the house and deserted me. There was no damn way to do the reassembly quickly. Each towel-load had to be nursed into the room and carefully laid out on papers spread across the table. The poor chandelier's frame looked like Charlie Brown's Christmas tree as I began hanging the ornaments. I worked my ass off, and hours later I was far from being finished. To make matters worse, it didn't look right.

One side looked like the land of the munchkins and the other side almost touched the table. I panicked as I glanced at the time knowing that Brik would be home soon, but I knew that I could close off the room, and he would never know anything because he never went into the dining room. I would have the next day to right the disaster.

I closed the doors to the dining room and started making a nice dinner, figuring I was saved, at least for awhile, and I could work on it for eight hours the next day. Like a drug-dog sniffing out trouble, Brik began to pace around when he got home.

For some reason, I guess I seemed nervous and he asked, "What did you do today? What did you wreck?"

He began thrashing around the house looking for trouble. One of the first places he checked was the garage. "Is the car okay?"

"Yes," I said. "What's wrong with you?

"Look, I know you fucked up something. Now what is it?"

"Nothing, you're so paranoid. Why do you think something is fucked up?"

He said, "Because I live with you. I know what it's like when you're content. When you're nervous about something, I also know what that's like."

All of a sudden, he flung open the doors to the dining room like he had sonar radar and after a stunned silence screamed, "You stupid jerk-off. Look at this thing. This chandelier...My God...You can piss away money faster than... first the tree, now the chandelier." His enraged commentary continued for quite a while.

I said, "I'll work on them tomorrow, but aren't they nice and clean? Don't they shine like diamonds?"

"Yes, but what good is it? It looks like something that should be trashed. Now you write the company and tell them you're a jerk-off, and get a diagram of this thing."

"How can I put that down?" I pleaded.

He literally made me sit down and write the Waterford company, telling them I was a jerk-off and to "please send me a diagram."

Their reply arrived two weeks later: "Dear Jerk-Off: enclosed is the diagram you requested ..."

The diagram helped some; every hole finally had something dangling from it, but the poor thing never looked as regal to me after that. No telling who's enjoying the masterpiece today.

30

DUCK

BRIK BEGAN TO GET A LITTLE COCKY. NOW THAT WE'D SETTLED into a relationship, he wasn't as attentive or respectful as he should have been, especially when his work schedule at the studio became more hectic and involved.

Meanwhile, I was becoming Julia Childs in the kitchen and had decided to prepare one of Brik's favorite dishes, duck à l'orange. Every detail of the dinner was thought out to perfection, from fresh asparagus, to the other delectables that had been delivered by Premier Market. I had taken cooking classes with Julia Childs and Wolfgang Puck and was putting it all to the test that evening.

That night I sent the house staff home early and rumbled around setting our finest Waterford crystal, Royal Doulton china, and silverware in the dining room under the dimmed, magnificent chandelier, and then I waited for Brik to arrive.

The champagne chilled, and the candles perched in the silver candlesticks flickered with anticipation. The salad forks and plates were in the freezer chilling, and the delicious smell of roasting duck filled the air with a mouth-watering hominess, creating a wonderful place for Brik to come home to.

He was supposed to be home at 8:00 p.m. With everything ready, I fell exhausted into my chair at the dining room table and reflected on the extravaganza that I had spent hours preparing. What a wonderful feeling of accomplishment and creativity that was.

By 8:30 p.m., he hadn't come home, nor had he bothered to call. By 9:00 p.m., no word yet. I made endless sweeps through the kitchen, and was tired of checking the damn shrinking duck and the front drive for his car. By 10:00 p.m., the bottle of champagne was floating in water, its label saturated and sliding off the bottle. My thoughts bent towards murder or at least grave injury. With every passing minute I became more enraged and I began slamming the refrigerator door until the jars in its doors rattled and rearranged themselves. Some even crashed to the floor.

Peeking into the oven door, I saw a shriveled duck that resembled a deflated football. I shrieked and fell into a crying fit, then lurched to the dining room, blew out the candles between sobs, and began a truly awesome destruction. The dinner had been the height of refinement and sophistication; now my primitive rage marked the polar opposite of a human's emotional experience. Jerking up the four corners of the lace tablecloth to contain the silverware, candles, china, and crystal, I dragged the bundle to the floor. And with a crashing violence I hauled it through the kitchen to the oven, where I slam-dunked the fucking duck and all the other dishes into this pile.

Again, I gathered the four corners together and began to kick the shit out of the swollen tablecloth as I continued to the back door. Much to my satisfaction I heard glass breaking and mysterious, distressed crunches as each foot kicked and stepped its way to the backyard. With my last strength, I twirled the leaking tablecloth around and around my head, then launched it into the swimming pool. Walking back to the house, I turned to see what looked like the remains of an airplane crash at sea. The saturated lace tablecloth was partly transparent, closing and spreading out on the waves of the splash. The duck floated quietly near the diving board.

About 1:00 a.m. Brik came reeling into the house yelling and slurring his words, "Where's my baby? Where's my duck? Where's my baby? Where's my duck?"

I raised my head from a teary pillow and told him where he could find his duck. "Your fucking duck is floating in the pool, you bastard!" I screamed. "What's with you? Where have you been? Have you no respect? You could have at least picked up a phone and called me!"

It cost $2,000 to clean out the glass from the pool, but it was worth it because he always called from that day on, even if he was going to be just a minute late to dinner.

I figure if you allow people to walk all over you, no matter what your position or stature in life, you might as well accept your position as a doormat and not complain when their feet use you as a transition from one place to another. By the way, duck was never served or spoken of again.

31

MOVE OUT

OUR HOME ON MOUNTAIN DRIVE REMAINED THE STAGE ON WHICH many emotional dramas were performed. From the comedic sublime to the ridiculous, hurtful psychological warfare, we indulged ourselves in any way we chose.

Indulgence, that became the theme song of those years. Money was no object, nor was status, and for years we were unfettered by the normal restrictions most people encounter along the road of life. We lived, fought, and loved in exaggerated ways. Our histrionics at least brought life back to the Mountain Drive neighborhood, nurtured curiosity, and stimulated conversations among the neighbors. At nightly dinner parties at places like Spagos, people repeated the latest and greatest sagas that had played out at our household. The "tree" and "duck" stories looped through Beverly Hills like a wave. The publicity-shy, bored, and cautious souls relished our occasionally fucked-up life.

I began to buy my clothes exclusively from Nieman Marcus, and, of course, incurred huge bills. In this I was encouraged by my own personal shopper, Gina Clark. She made the downward, decadent spending spiral ever so much fun.

"Tony, you must come get this new Versace shirt," she would phone. "See you later."

I would speed to the store and get one in every color at $1,200 a piece. No wonder Brik got miffed when the bills came in.

One morning, he reviewed the monthly bills and really started yelling about the excesses and the extravagance of my clothing bills. The argument escalated into a picture-rattling yelling match. We each got into some good verbal punches, but the knockout blow was issued by Brik, "Just get your guinea-ass out of here and back to the gutter of New Jersey where you belong. Get the fuck out of here before I'm back from work." I fell silent. The argument was over, so was our life together.

No one talks to me like that. As soon as Brik's car squealed out of the driveway, I called Bekins Movers and spoke to a Maryann. "How long does it take to move a seventeen-room house?" I inquired.

"About two to two-and-a-half days, sir," she said.

"Well, get a crew over here now. You have seven hours."

We moved everything out of the house, including the light bulbs and the garage door connection. If I'd had the time, I would have drained the pool, uprooted the sod, and pulled up the wall-to-wall carpet. The nerve of him telling me to get my guinea-ass out of the home that I had lovingly decorated and painstakingly cared for.

Unfortunately, Regent Airlines was booked up and I couldn't catch a flight out of LA that evening. On top of Brik's clothes that I had piled up in the middle of the floor, I left him a note saying I'd be in the Swanlake Suite at the Bel Air Hotel if he wanted to talk to me.

Naturally, the huge moving uproar hadn't gone unnoticed by the neighbors. I told them that he'd ordered my guinea-ass out of town, and they said, "Oh, he didn't mean it, Tony." But nothing they said stopped the evacuation. Finally, the swollen truck pulled out of the driveway. With a weak wave to the neighbors, I left my home and my love. I was too tired to cry.

I later heard that when Brik came home the neighbors (who were hiding in the bushes) heard him roar with laughter when he tried the garage opener and nothing happened. The neighbors burst out of their hiding places and clustered around him, and as he opened the front door, they told him all the details.

"Tony's gone!" the neighbors declared.

"No, he's not. Look, here's a note that says he's at the Swanlake Suite."

The neighbors just shook their heads, parked the tale into a "must-tell" category for the next party and shuffled home to their realm of normality.

He called me (I didn't have time to disconnect the phones) and said, "Tony, I really love you and I am sorry for what I said. You are the funniest person. You know I didn't mean what I said. Please call up and get everything back."

"I can't, it's the weekend. We can't get it back until Monday. Come on over, and we'll spend the weekend here and have room service." He came right over, and we had a wonderful weekend just holed up in the luxurious Swanlake Suite. On Monday I called and had the furnishings returned and considered the $12,000 move a great lesson for Brik.

Because we had wealth, we fought differently than those who aren't as financially well off. We fought in creative ways that would really make an impact. Now that I look back on it, everything was so out of proportion and out of control. Our revenge was only limited by our imagination, and I have never been accused of lacking in that department.

32

Babs

The arrangement Brik and I had concerning our sexual relationship would be baffling to most people because he really loved women, and I didn't care. Yet our relationship and love for each other was rock solid. By the way, I was faithful to him for more than 24 years, even though he married several times and always had strong attractions to women.

As strange as it seems, I wasn't jealous of his numerous heterosexual relationships, nor did I feel slighted when he began dating and later married one of the world's most beautiful women. I wanted him to have what he needed and desired.

In return for my faithfulness, I lived a life of luxury and had all I needed and almost anything I wanted. I had the freedom to fly to New York and stay in our apartment, visit my family at any time, and, if I chose, walk the beaches near our Florida home on the intra-coastal waterway. Extravagant summer trips to the south of France were sometimes shared with Brik and always shared with dear friends. More about those times later.

Brik's popularity was soaring as his movies and television shows scored hit after hit. He was, as they say, at the top of his game. Whenever Brik became obsessed with someone (like me, for instance, and later the model, Wallace Ford), he pursued them until he had won them over.

Our Beverly Hills home was entirely too large, and with his impending marriage to Wallace, we sold it and moved out. I chose a penthouse in Century Park East that needed some renovation for my next residence. While the work was being done, I moved into an apartment in Westwood known as Woodcliff, and it was here that I met Babs.

Babette "Babs" Carlton was a striking showgirl dancer with a group called the "Dancing Machine." There was no doubt about it—she wasn't a librarian. When Bette Midler sings, "Pretty legs and great big knockers, that's what sells the tickets at the door," she could have been talking about Babs Carlton.

Everything about Babs was fun and exaggerated: her height, lips, boobs, hair, nails, and personality. What great memories I have of our friendship and of the sexual stories she told about many of the most popular stars.

Babs was always an adventure-in-progress with a collection of day-to-day items accompanying her in the trunk of her black Z28 sports car. In a way, she reminded me of a cross between Janis Joplin and a Vegas showgirl because she had the wild, carefree spirit of Joplin as well as a definite showgirl aura. As she motored about with her necessities close at hand, she never knew where she might be each night and certainly could never predict when she might need her beaded dresses, furs, jewelry, and flashy high heels.

Her sexual escapades were legendary, at least in my mind. I loved to watch her stroll across a Las Vegas casino floor and see the place drop dead. She could cause a stir just by walking through the high-roller betting areas where tens of thousands of dollars were at stake. Everything just stopped when she appeared. It was no wonder she had her pick of men.

Babs' nomadic nature led her to be gone for days at a time. Her life had no set patterns and her friends learned to stifle panic attacks when she couldn't be reached at her apartment. As we all figured out some time along the way, she would occasionally blow in from the cold and treat us to some damn good stories. One late night call awoke me with a cheery "Hi. You won't believe what happened to me this time, doll."

"Babs? It's fucking 3:00 a.m."

"I know, love, but I couldn't wait to tell you what happened tonight. You know how much I've been hot for Robert? Well, tonight I got my stab at him. Tony, I was so excited after rubbing up against him for the last week. Am I ragged or what?"

"What? What happened?"

"Tony, he was all potatoes and no meat. My thumb could have done a better job. I could have died. Well, better go, love ya."

"Love ya, too," I just stared into the phone, laughed, and dropped back to sleep. Poor Babs, she just hated vegetarians.

During this time, Babs and I were hired for an MGM science fiction thriller. Every day we had to be on the set at 6:00 a.m. For six months we worked on the movie, but if you blinked you'd miss my part. Even so, it was wonderful to have the paycheck, prestige, and new friends. We really enjoyed the experience and the time we got to spend together.

Finally, my Century Park East penthouse was ready, and I moved in. On the back lots of 20th Century Fox, property had been sold off and this area became known as Century City. The Century Plaza hotel was the centerpiece of the development, which also had theaters, shops, and some great restaurants within walking distance from my penthouse.

I was 21 at the time and heard many comments as I moved in such as "Your father must be very wealthy to put you in the penthouse." The two-bedroom, two-bath penthouse was lovely with its westward view of the ocean. At night, I would stand on the terrace and watch the lights of LAX airport, deeply enjoying living in my own place.

I had completely decorated the penthouse with the luxuries and styles of the times. The kitchen and bedroom were all white. For the living area, I chose a plush lemon-yellow carpet; cream suede leather furniture; and lots of chrome, glass, and mirrors. It was, after all, the seventies.

Many great people lived in the twin towers of Century Park, including influential actresses, actors, directors, and entertainers. One day shortly after I moved in, I had the door open and was on my knees doing something to the carpet when a vaguely familiar woman approached. She was so very thin, blond, and delicate.

She said, "I was wondering....May I come in?"

I said, "Of course."

"I was wondering who was putting in this lemon-yellow carpet. They said it was the handsome young man up in the penthouse."

She never told me her name, but it turned out to be Lana Turner, who lived on the floor below me in the corner unit. We later became very good friends.

33

HATTIE

LIFE IN THE PENTHOUSE SETTLED INTO SOME FAMILIAR ROUTINES that included visiting various neighbors like Lydia Snyder. Lydia and I began what eventually became a 20-year friendship. Even though she was in her mid-70s when we met, we didn't let a 50-year gap interfere with our friendship. She lived on the first floor of the building, and several times a week I would drop in for a visit.

Lydia was so full of fun and movie history. Her daughter had married the son of Harry Stradling, a great Oscar-winning director of photography for the studios. One of his most famous movies was *My Fair Lady*. She had divorced her husband, and her boyfriend had died some years before I met her. During my frequent visits she would entertain me with old Hollywood stories over a glass of wine, and I would share my adventures with her. At this point I was on my own and at times it was a bit lonely, so it was good to be surrounded by lovely people such as Lydia.

Not long after I moved into the penthouse, I answered a knock at the door. An African-American, Mammy-like figure announced, "My name is Hattie Lincoln. I'm here to take care of you, and take care of you I will." She swept by me with purposeful flair, her eyes scoping out her new domain as she entered my living room and my heart.

She was a plentiful woman: plenty of spirit, advice, energy, razor wit, loyalty, and breasts that were her pride and joy. They came around the corner long before she did. Some said they looked like torpedoes. In a way, they defined her, as though she thought of them as a piled up plate of warm chocolate chip cookies permanently attached to her chest that everyone wanted to get their hands or mouths on.

"Tony, see that guy over there? He's looking at my titties." People were always looking at her titties.

Brik had sent her to be my house servant, but she quickly became a close companion and confidante. She was a treasure, a delight, and one of the funniest people I've met in my life. Together we occupied the penthouse and would banter back and forth, just cracking each other up with comments. I became "her boy." She became a best, lifelong friend.

Hattie was in her late 50s when she came to work for me. Actually, I don't like the way that sounds because she was much more than a house servant. She was a dear friend who looked out for me, did the cooking and cleaning, and helped me entertain. What endeared her to me was her loyalty and her sense of humor, which was just a riot.

Along with her loving nature coexisted a powerful confrontational spirit. Hattie loved a good fight, loved to get her dander up, and cause a commotion. She had been raised in St. Louis and was familiar with wielding a razor, just like all the other girls who grew up in her neighborhood. Her nickname in the building was "Mohammed Hattie."

The laundry room was in the basement of Century Park East. A thriving subculture of domestics intermingled with the sloshing washers and spinning dryers, their conversations fueled with outrageous tales about their employers. If appliances had ears, they would have been booked on the *Oprah Show*.

One day Hattie was in the laundry room washing and drying "her boy's" clothes. In her devotion to me, she carefully performed every chore to perfection. That day Hattie and Maria Garcia were the only people doing laundry. They hadn't bothered exchanging pleasantries. Their minds were on getting their chores completed and back upstairs for the afternoon television soaps.

Hattie was a few steps ahead of Maria in that she'd had her laundry out of the washers and into the dryers when Maria had begun. With a careful, thorough motion, Hattie wiped down the folding counter. She didn't want the fresh clothes to get messed up. Maria had plopped down into a scratched, metal folding chair with a two-month-old *National Enquirer*. Hattie opened the still revolving dryer to check the clothes. Perfect.

She gathered them up and gently heaped them onto the folding table when Maria uncrossed her skinny swinging leg and rested it on the edge of the folding table, where it was soon joined by its mate. The two feet together, one foot crossed on top of the other, fluttered a bit, just daring Hattie to do something about them.

A powerful blow dislodged those bony feet and sent them crashing to the cement floor. Maria flung the *Enquirer* up into the florescent lights and lunged over the mountain of warm clothes at Hattie. That was the wrong thing to do. Hattie's adolescent training really came into play that day. The only weapons she had were her hands, but then they were enough.

With one swift motion, she wrapped her fist into Maria's long hair and played crack the whip with her. Streams of Spanish screeched through the air until Hattie split Maria's lip with her other fist. Several people walked in on the battle and began screaming, "Two maids is fighting! Two maids is fighting!"

The awful commotion alerted the building security, and Hattie had to be calmed down and dragged off to the building superintendent's office. The poor Mexican girl was taken to Century City medical center for stitches. I was called to the superintendent's office when I got home and was shocked to see Hattie sitting there like a reprimanded school child. She leaned toward me and said softly, "That fucking Mexican didn't have any right sticking her nasty feet on my boy's clothes."

To make a long story short, Hattie had so endeared herself to the people there, it went off without incident. Of course, I paid for the stitches and medical bills. But from that day on, Hattie always seemed to have the laundry room to herself. No one seemed to have to do laundry when she was there. She would say, "Tony, it's so lonely doing laundry down there. Why do you suppose no one comes down when I'm doing clothes?"

"I haven't a clue."

34

PENTHOUSE

THE MANSELLS LIVED ON THE 10TH FLOOR OF CENTURY PARK East. Mr. Mansell was a popular producer in Hollywood and I met him at various parties shortly after I moved into the penthouse. For some reason he frequently mentioned that he was anxious that I meet his wife.

One day Hattie and I were on the elevator with an old woman who recognized me as the guy her husband had been telling her about. Mrs. Mansell introduced herself and invited me for cocktails and a visit at the end of the month. She glanced at Hattie and I introduced her to Mrs. Mansell. Domestics were not supposed to use the public elevators in Century Park East, but Hattie's popularity and reputation (not to mention her fists) seemed to exclude her from that rule.

Several weeks later, Hattie and I were riding the elevator to our 21st-floor penthouse when Mrs. Mansell joined us. I nodded and smiled at Mrs. Mansell, but quickly detected a hateful glare in her eyes.

"What are you doing in here?" she demanded, staring at Hattie.

"Excuse me?" Hattie asked.

"You servants are supposed to use the other elevators," Mrs. Mansell fired back.

"Excuse me?" I said, and she turned to me.

"Who are you?"

I said, "What?"

Hattie took a deep breath and expanded her ample chest, turned to her, and said, "Who are you? You crazy, blond, makeup-wearing bitch, you just spoke to him a couple of weeks ago and told him to come for cocktails. What's wrong with you? Are you crazy?"

She made Hattie get out and called the security men on her. Perhaps she was experiencing the beginning stages of Alzheimer's disease. I couldn't figure it out. Ironically, Hattie later worked some for the Mansells and over time she and Mrs. Mansell became good friends. Hattie would go down to her apartment for tea in the afternoons, and they would talk for hours. The poor thing was lonely and crazy. What a combination.

One day Hattie came hustling through the door with double news after visiting Mrs. Mansell. She couldn't wait to tell me that when she placed the tea cups in the dishwasher Mrs. Mansell said. "Oh, noooo, I never use the dishwasher. The noise of it scares me."

Also, that was the day Mrs. Mansell confided that if Hattie ever saw yellow sheets on the bed, she would know that she had given Mr. Mansell some pussy the night before. Boy, were we tempted to check, but, of course, we never got the chance.

A very beautiful woman, Patricia Crosby, lived across the hall. She was the ex-daughter-in-law of the old pipe-smoking crooner, Bing Crosby. Most of the public never knew what a stern, demanding father he had been. Patricia had divorced Bing's son years before I moved in.

I met Liza Minnelli one afternoon at Patricia's apartment. I asked if it was lonely traveling and performing in distant cities, and then going back to the hotel with only room service to look forward to. She only smiled, but I quickly saw that Hollywood wasn't all it was cracked up to be. Even with all of the glory and the fame, it could be a very lonely life.

35

FRIENDS

SOON AFTER I MOVED INTO THE PENTHOUSE, I WANTED TO GET out and meet other people. It wasn't that I was looking for sex or a relationship because I had all of that I needed; I was simply interested in meeting new friends and having new experiences. Besides, I was also getting a little tired of being with straight people all the time, and I began to feel adventuresome. I had heard about a place called the Gallery Room, a bar on Santa Monica Boulevard, so one spring afternoon I climbed into my Corvette and went cruising for fun.

I was young, tan and in great shape with thick, medium-length, chestnut-colored hair. I wore about two cents worth of clothes: a cropped half-shirt with a tiny logo over the left breast that read "Body by God," skimpy micro-shorts, knee socks, and ultra-white sneakers. As soon as I got out of the car, appreciative whistles pierced the air. Imagine a fresh packaged chicken with a Corvette thrown in, too.

It was like someone yelled "Freeze" when I walked across the room, and that's not just my memory, either, because on that particular day, I was to get my first glimpse of Phil Sloan and Michael Carmenetti, who subsequently became lifelong friends. Actually, I don't remember seeing them, but they were there, and several weeks later Phil told me that he had certainly seen me that day and remembered the stir I caused.

On entering the Gallery Room, a handsome, blond guy came up to me and asked me what I was drinking. I said, "Dom Perignon." He went to the bar and ordered a $100 bottle that was quickly delivered to us along with two chilled glasses.

Phil and Michael watched from across the room, silently cheering their friend on in his pursuit of me. After I drank about three sips and thanked him, I walked out of the bar, got into my Corvette, and drove away. I was oblivious to his friends' scrutiny; I had simply decided to leave because I was bored and ready to go home.

But the saga continued. In early summer my friend Bette came to visit me, and I suggested we go eat lunch at the Garden District Restaurant, a popular gay restaurant on La Cienega Boulevard. The lines were always long at the Garden District, where lush flowers and plants woven through lattice-work partitioned the indoor and outdoor eating areas. It was very small and intimate—the bar along the entire right side and private booths on the left. As usual the place was packed, but as Bette and I walked up the steps of the restaurant, I heard a scream.

"That's him. That's him, everybody. That's the boy who ragged on Tim." Everyone began applauding wildly. Phil Sloan rose from his table and said, "You don't remember us, but please, please, come over to our table." Bette and I joined the group and were quickly given a retroactive replay of the Dom Perignon incident from their perspective.

"We were there the night you came into the Gallery Room, and Tim ordered that $100 bottle of champagne. Do you realize that was the biggest hoot we've had for so long?"

I asked innocently, "What do you mean?"

He explained that when you accept a drink from someone at a bar, it is kind of an indication that you're interested in them, to pursue, to date, or whatever. He said, "Here you had three sips and stuck him for a hundred bucks. It was just a big laugh. We've been dying about it for weeks."

Little did I know that that innocent incident would put into motion a series of chapters in my book of experiences. Nestled into the wine-colored booths sat Phil Sloan, Michael Carmenetti, Steven Ashton, and Bob Welsh. Bette and I felt instantly welcomed, yet under curious examination.

They treated me as if I was a new dessert just arriving at the table. I quickly launched into some of my stories and felt their appreciative eyes absorb my every little flare of expression. They drank me in with their intellectual eyes, and I loved it.

At first, they seemed like a laughing panel of judges gathering evidence of my worth and wit. Apparently I passed, because their gavel of approval soon smashed onto the table, and I became one of their constant companions. My new acquaintances felt like old friends.

Phil Sloan, first in the booth (and to this day, first in my heart) was the glue that held the group together. What I liked best about him was that he thought I was a piss; I cracked him up. Phil is a well-educated, refined man, extremely successful in business, and he had bought a magnificent house in Hollywood Land under the "H" in the famous Hollywood hillside sign.

The house had been built by Busby Berkley, a famous choreographer and producer known for his movie extravaganzas in the 20s and 30s. His were the movies in which tap dancers tapped themselves into a frenzy. For some reason, whenever Phil looked at me, I wanted to make sure he wasn't disappointed. His piercing eyes twinkling or tearing up at my antics made me deeply happy.

He was thin and often wore impeccable clothing that was slightly oversized. He almost disappeared into his clothes, as if to set himself apart from the scene so that he could become an observer instead of a participant. Eventually, however, after many others had told their tales, Phil could absolutely dominate the conversation with his perceptive, cutting wit. His elegance and dead-on humor totally captivated me, and we became friends for eternity.

Even though time and space have separated us, Phil and I have continued our close friendship with calls, visits, and laughter-filled letters. He has been a friend through thick and thin, never wavering nor parceling out his friendship in a controlling way. He has made no demands on me in return for his love and loyalty. Phil is the epitome of what a friend should be. I feel that God placed him in my life as a living example of unconditional love.

Next was Michael. He was a living tribute to absolute perfection in a Max Factor kind of way. His eyes were quick to catch discrete nuances of emotions and subtleties of fashion. It was entertaining to watch his reactions to interior design atrocities and to listen to his creative solutions for them. And had the other grand queen, Queen Elizabeth, ever caught a glimpse of his matching leather handbags, there would have been trouble.

Michael's every outfit suggested a flair. His richly textured, fine silk garments were masterfully draped on his well-built frame. He was fond of black with occasional rich cream accents and usually wore a slightly blousey shirt with a gold necklace and an elegant coat resting lightly on his shoulders. No doubt about it, he was a GG, a Grand Girl, and the best interior designer in Hollywood. We called him "Miss C" (for Carmenetti).

Towering Steven Ashton and Bob Welsh rounded out the group that met nightly at the Garden District for cocktails. These were the days of drinking and drugs, but heavy drinking was our only vice then. Whenever I could, I joined them for cocktails.

One night Phil and Steven got drunk as hell. Of course, they hadn't eaten anything and proceeded to get in their cars and head for home. Steven got to West Hollywood and La Cienega Boulevard before smashing into a Volkswagen that burst into flames. People were screaming and pulling each other out of the wreck, and Steven was handcuffed and taken to West Hollywood jail. Thank heavens, no one was hurt.

Phil drove his white "Jenny Jaguar" home by way of Sunset Boulevard and Franklin, where he passed out at a stoplight. Cops were alerted to the prolonged blowing horn and came to investigate. When they opened the door, Phil's head slid off the steering wheel, and he slumped to the pavement. He was also handcuffed and thrown into the Beverly Hills jail.

Both Phil and Steven were allowed one call from jail and each unsuccessfully tried calling the other. Phil was escorted into a holding cell with eight other guys who scurried from him like rats from an exterminator because he decided he'd give them all blow jobs. Before the objects of his affection could be separated from him, Phil managed to score once. One crippled prisoner with a broken leg couldn't limp away fast enough, and he gracefully accepted the offer.

The next morning when they were sober, they were released. Each was livid thinking his best friend had let him down; had, in fact, probably been with someone he'd picked up that night. Both were churning inside thinking, "Dumb bitch, you scored. Sure, a trick was better than me. Didn't answer my fucking call."

They both cleaned up and went to work. Steven, who worked for Phil at his computer company, stormed into Phil's office, slammed the door behind him and said, "You hussy bitch. Where were you last night?"

"What? Where were you?" Phil replied. "And lower your voice, I still have a headache."

"I was in jail, thank you very much," replied Steven.

Phil said, "Me, too!"

Both forgot their hangovers and fell over screaming and laughing. That story became an instant classic.

36

PUSSY SOUFFLÉ

EVEN THOUGH BRIK WAS FIRST IN MY LIFE, I ENJOYED THE COMPANY of my new friends as often as I could. Almost every afternoon, Michael, Phil, Steven, and Bob went to the Garden District for cocktails, dinner, and laughs. Whenever I was able to, I joined them, and we became quite a rat pack.

We had the most fun together, taking turns being the center of attention. Not everyone was as book-smart as Phil; however, they all had a comedic intellect that was in the Mensa range. Razor wit and astute observations bounced around the table like pinballs. The gut laughter was addictive and constant as we reviewed the day.

It was an emotional, highly charged combination of friends who had found an appreciative audience for their humor. Sometimes, however, less amicable feelings surfaced. Occasionally I would be alerted to the dreaded sound of ice being rattled forcefully in a glass, and I knew to duck. Petty jealousies could erupt when a good-looking guy came into view and several of the group's interest was piqued.

Invariably I would hear, "I saw him first, now butt out." Then came the agitated clinking of ice, followed by an airborne drink thrown by the one who felt he had first discovered the find. These outbursts never amounted to anything, except to add another great story to our ever-growing list of escapades.

Around Halloween, Michael and a group he was in known as the GGRC (Gay Girls' Riding Club) prepared for their annual gay benefit extravaganza held at the Palladium. Of course, I wanted to attend, but Brik was opposed. However, I demanded to go and went anyway, and it was well worth it to see Michael and the other GGRC's in their tutus and the other queens who came in outrageous outfits. One "girl" showed up wearing a ball gown with some kind of strings sewn to it, and when he pulled the strings, the dress rose up over his head and became a pumpkin that lit up. Everyone screamed, applauded, and jumped up and down. What I enjoyed most about associating with this group was being immersed in such a creative and colorful atmosphere. They lived to laugh and defy convention. They were human exclamation points.

Phil helped educate me in some of the finer things such as wine appreciation. He treated the group to lunch one day at the Bistro, one of the most beautiful and stateliest restaurants in Beverly Hills. Besides the usual group, a lady by the name of Jan Burgano—a magnificent southern beauty—joined us that day. She had red hair and blue eyes and was being kept by one of the wealthiest men in San Francisco. We quickly became fast friends.

Phil ordered a fabulous French wine called "Pouilly Fuisse." It was so delicious, we drank glass after glass and got plastered. Sometime during lunch I decided I would surprise Brik and order "Pouilly Fuisse" for everyone that night when we went to Nick's Fish Market with Gene Hackman and his wife. Brik would be pleased and impressed with my new, expanded horizons. Over and over, Phil repeated the hard to pronounce name until I had it committed to memory. It was going to wreck everyone that I knew the name of such a pissy French wine.

Brik was waiting for me when I arrived at the penthouse. As I hurriedly changed for the evening, he said, "Come on, come on, we're going to be late."

"Just wait, you're going to be so proud of me tonight."

"Yeah, yeah, I'm always proud of you. Now hurry up, let's go."

Nick's Fish Market was a seafood restaurant on Sunset Boulevard known for its exquisite food and private circular booths. Celebrities were fond of eating at Nick's because they could enjoy seclusion in the rounded, cocoon-like booths that had private lighting and music controls. The patrons could also count on having the same waiter and busboy every time they came to dine.

Brik, Gene Hackman, his lovely wife, and I were seated at our usual booth when the wine steward approached Brik and asked if he wanted to order a bottle of wine that evening. Brik replied that yes, he did.

"May I please do the honors?" I said.

"What? What are you talking about?" Brik stared.

"I would like to order the wine tonight."

He just looked, smiled, and crinkled up his nose as if to say, "Yeah, right, what's this going to be?"

I turned to the wine steward and said, "I would like to order" (my mind was searching for that pissy French name) "yes, I would like to order a bottle of "Pussy Soufflé." Everyone screamed.

Brik burst in, "What are you trying to say!?"

"I, I don't know. It was something's pussy."

"What? You don't know what you want!"

"Yes, I do. Bring us a bottle of no one's pussy, Blue Nun."

The "Pussy Soufflé" story looped around Hollywood for years after that. In fact, one Thursday night we were in Matteos, an exclusive Italian restaurant on Westwood Boulevard, when a bottle of Pouille Fuisse wine was sent to our table from Connie Stevens and Rock Hudson. The label had been scratched out and changed to read "Pussy Soufflé." The legend continued.

37

GIRLS

Now, for some of the "girl" stories. All of us "girls" had nicknames; for example, Steven was "Madame Puss," Phil was "Miss Sloan," Michael Carmenetti was "Miss C," or just "C," and I was known as "Pretty." We also referred to each other using feminine pronouns "she" and "her." Everyone could be a "bitch" or a "guinea," too.

Even our cars were given pet names. My Corvette was "Connie." Phil's new Jaguar was "Jenny," and Michael had a new El Dorado Cadillac named "Elizabeth." Steven's old coughing Mustang, "Sally," rounded out the group.

One afternoon we all piled into Sally and set out for an enjoyable excursion. Steven was mortified that his car was such a bomb, but none of the rest of us cared (even though she was leaving a trail of black smoke up and down Wilshire Boulevard). We just thought it was a hoot. That is, until we were caught in traffic congestion on Hollywood Boulevard.

Crowds had gathered for some premiere and with limousines stretched around the block, the car stalled out right in front of the theater. Steven tried to crank the bitch, but all she did was choke, cough, and spew out smoke and gas fumes while making the most awful sounds. It was like Sally had decided to die with an audience. We were also dying, with laughter, even though Steven was in a jerk doing everything he knew to do to get her rolling again.

It was like a bad "B" movie with an overly dramatic death scene that goes on and on. Sally would shiver to life, then rattle and spew, and drop dead again. There was nothing we could do but laugh; however, the pissy crowd soon came alive with its own opinions of what we should do with Sally.

"Park that piece of shit," mouthed a guy in a tuxedo.

"Yeah," roared others in line. "Get that bitch out of here."

Stuff began bouncing off Sally's chipped blue paint job. People were actually pelting us with programs, wadded up cigarette packs, and anything else they could get their hands on. Eventually, Sally lurched away, her tail pipe between her wheels, and Steven traded her in for another piece of shit. Poor thing, he always got stiffed with cars.

Old man Bob Welsh (who has since passed on and is probably entertaining the angels) used to crack us up with some of his outrageous footwear. At parties when we were distracted by music and laughter and least expected it, someone would roar out, "Look at Bob!" Sixty-seven-year-old skinny Bob would be flipping burgers with his pants rolled up, wearing red satin, 6-inch stiletto heels. Those red pumps came out at all the important occasions and became, in our crowd, as famous as the ruby slippers.

Michael, with all of his style and sense of class, was a great influence on me. From him I learned more about how to entertain and how to choose the finer things in life, and I appreciate him for that. One of the things I didn't learn from him but did enjoy doing with him was taking the drug "poppers."

"Poppers," actually amyl nitrate, were popular with the gay community for the sexual high they caused. But "C" and I used to take a hit just to get a quick high and laugh. He would take me into his kitchen, open up cabinets, exposing countless sets of gorgeous china and crystal. We would scream with laughter. Sometimes he would throw open his wardrobe doors and expose his numerous fur coats, enough for the Rockettes in December. We would roar, howl, collapse on his bed, and roll about like little boys who had just played a prank. It was his way of showing me what he had, but it was such a hoot how he did it.

I was a novice when I became friends with these guys, and now I realize what a big influence they had on me, especially "C," because I ended up like him with many sets of china, crystal, flatware, and fur coats, too.

Around Christmas time I would get cranked up for the holidays, which always meant lots of parties and travel home to be with my family in New Jersey. Brik accompanied me for several Christmas holidays, but after he married, I traveled home without him. Which was fine with me because I was totally comfortable with our arrangement and thought I had the best of both worlds. Brik and I always celebrated Christmas near New Year's after we'd both completed our family obligations.

Every year Phil Sloan had an elaborate tree-trimming party, complete with valet parking. One Christmas all of the friends gathered at Phil's Spanish-style estate for the big event and quickly began indulging in champagne, served in Baccarat crystal glasses. Michael's black limousine glided up to the front walk and we all hurried to the circular vestibule to greet him. The large room had a 14-foot ceiling, a Spanish-tiled floor, and a beautiful round table topped with an exquisite flower arrangement.

Michael emerged from the back of the limo wearing a new mink coat and walked theatrically into the house to wild applause from the guests. His French slippers glided him forward in the grandest of style. Encouraged by his reception, he raised his mink-covered arm up to his face, only showing his dramatic eyes, like the ad in the *Vogue* magazine, "What becomes of a legend?" He twirled several times in grandeur and sashayed around and around the table. Finally, he flung his coat to the floor and kicked it into the corner. The crowd was ecstatic. "C" knew how to make an entrance.

Sure, we were there to have fun, but we also had the mission of trimming Phil's tree. Music flooded the room with cheer, and waiters dispersed their own variety. Before long, we were feeling quite in the holiday spirit.

We stood about the enormous tree carefully placing ornaments, balls (we liked to say that word), garland, and lights in the most perfect places. It looked stunning. "Enough, enough for this side," declared Phil as he rotated it around. As the evening progressed we began to get careless and just started throwing garland and balls onto the tree. There must be a strong negative correlation to being artistic and being shitfaced because that side of the tree looked like Charlie Brown's tree and became destined to be turned toward the wall that Christmas season.

The party was somewhat marred by the fact that Phil's handsome lover, Trent, had decided he needed some space and was absent for the celebrations. Christmas is not the time to be ditched by a lover. We could all relate to that and felt compassion for him, but Phil just said, "Fuck him." As the party wore on, however, I could feel Phil sliding into a deeper state of self-pity.

Near the end of the evening, about ten of us gathered at the marble fireplace in the great room to assess the tree trimming accomplishment and to toast the end to a perfect party. We were still drinking from Phil's new Baccarat crystal glasses (easily worth $200 each.) when I heard Phil yell "Oh, go fuck yourself, Trent!" and he hurled his glass against the marble fireplace. Michael grabbed his glass, drained it dry, licked it around the rim, and smashed it, saying, "Fuck you, Trent!" I did the same thing. We all screamed, "Fuck you, Trent!" and joined in on the expensive plundering. Oh, the crystal carnage that evening.

The next morning Phil called crying and saying we had busted up 22 of his precious glasses. "How drunk were we? I only have two left."

38

RESCUE

ONE CHRISTMAS PHIL, MICHAEL, AND I DECIDED TO MEET IN NEW York City. They registered at The Plaza Hotel, while I stayed at our apartment on Sutton and 56th Street. There's nothing quite like Christmas in New York, with its mind-boggling array of lights, decorations, and music. From Michael's room on the tenth floor of the Plaza, it was fun to watch the bundled up pedestrians jostling their way up and down the streets carrying Christmas gifts for friends and family.

That first evening the three of us had a lovely dinner at the Giraffe and, needless to say, we drank too much. After dinner, we all decided to go change out of our suits into something more comfortable and to go partying at a gay bar called Uncle Charlie's.

It didn't take much for Phil or me to get ready. But, we quickly saw that it was going to be a while for Michael to check his eyeliner and makeup, to make sure that every eyelash was in place, and to do a "number" on his hair. We were impatient and told him, "Look 'C,' we're not waiting for you. We're going on. We'll catch you there. Grab a cab. You know where we're going."

Michael never showed up. We waited two hours and began to get concerned. "We'd better go back and see what's going on," I finally decided.

Phil replied, "If I know Michael, he's probably met somebody, the doorman maybe. He's probably got someone shoved up against a palm tree having sex."

We got a cab and retraced our route to the hotel; however, long before we arrived at the hotel, we saw search lights sweeping across the cold December sky. Must be a premiere or the Radio City Music Hall promotional, I thought, but as we approached the Plaza, we saw and heard an enormous commotion.

Some people were screaming, "Jump! Jump lady."

Others yelled imploringly, "Hold on. God loves you. It's Christmas, for God's sake."

We lowered the windows and craned our necks to focus in on the excitement. A policeman with a heavy-duty loudspeaker was sending up words of encouragement: "Things will get better, lady. Don't jump." He put down the horn, shook his head, and said, "Poor thing, she must be crazy."

We couldn't even get close to the front of the Plaza because of all the fire trucks, police, and emergency vehicles. We finally just jumped out of the cab and hastened up the sidewalk, pushing aside the sea of shoppers before we could see what all the fuss was about.

When we got close enough to see what was going on, we followed the frantically pointing fingers of the crowd and saw a woman standing on a tenth-floor ledge in a flapping Chinese robe. She stood pressed to the building and illuminated by the wildly circling, blinding white lights. Little puffs of frigid air blew out of her mouth as she screamed, "Help me. Help me." Norma Desmond had nothing on her.

We asked some policeman what was going on and he replied, "Some woman is trying to commit suicide."

I looked up again and recognized Michael's Chinese robe and gasped, "That's not a woman. That's Michael!" Phil and I frantically rushed to Michael's room along with the paramedics, firemen, and emergency rescue units.

Police broke into Michael's room and bashed down the bathroom door which was sealed shut. They made a human chain and pulled the hysterical Michael back through the window. When the rescue team eased him off the narrow ledge and into the window, the crowd simultaneously cheered and booed and slowly dispersed into the night, some disappointed, and some relieved.

It turned out that a pipe in the bathroom had begun spewing out deadly hot steam while Michael was putting on his makeup and he had gotten trapped in the damp bathroom when the door had become stuck. He couldn't escape. His only hope was to climb out the bathroom window and wait on the ledge for help.

Phil and I skidded into his room just as the second wave of paramedics rolled out a hideous creature strapped on a gurney. Michael looked like something the cat had dragged in with his makeup running and his curly hair hanging and dangling off of the medic's pillow.

"I'll kill you 'girls' when I have enough strength. You have no idea what I've been through tonight," he whined as he was rolled out.

A news cameraman followed them to the ambulance. "C" bravely raised his limp hand and said, "I'm ready for my close up, Mr. DeMille."

For all of you people who were at the Plaza that December night, now you know the real story.

39

CINCO DE MAYO

MICHAEL BEGAN DATING RYAN NOBLE, A SET DESIGNER FROM ONE of the big movie studios, when some of his circle of friends tried to move into our whirlwind existence by inviting us to parties and events. While their eager friendliness seemed complimentary on the surface, many times I felt that there were ulterior motives because of the celebrity of our group. Everyone knew I was being kept by a famous star, "C" was at the top of the interior decorator and design industry, and Phil was head of an influential business and later a university. At least in the gay community we were the cat's ass, and many were attracted to us because of that.

One such poor soul was a friend of Ryan Noble's named Raoul Diaz. The group was invited to Raoul's tiny apartment on the other side of Hollywood for the May 5th celebration known as Cinco de Mayo. We had reluctantly accepted the invitation and the closer we got to Raoul's place that afternoon, the rattier everything looked out of the shiny windows of Connie Corvette. Bits of paper and debris blew up as I sped by. A little doubt reared its ugly head, but I was always up for an adventure, never knew when another great story would appear. This was to be my lucky day.

Raoul absolutely glowed with excitement as he waved us in through his paint-chipped doorway. Pulsating Mexican music burst through the walls and out into the street. We yelled, "Hello. No, no trouble finding it." Michael was first to spot the red pottery bull in the corner under the shadow of the sombrero and woven striped blanket nailed to the wall.

"Nice touch," he noted.

We sidled around the glass-topped coffee table and tried to make ourselves comfortable in what seemed like a foreign country. A huge Mexican flag hung next to a picture of The Last Supper. Jesus on a crucifix hung over the archway into the dining room.

"What would you like to drink?" Raoul asked.

"C" wanted a scotch. I'd have a Harvey Wallbanger. Steven asked for vodka, and Bob wanted straight gin on the rocks. But all he had was sangria or beer. Raoul had no hard liquor in the house and we all did a quick eye-check to register our surprise.

"Come on girls, let's go to the liquor store and get it," Michael said.

Poor Raoul anguished for a moment and apologized, finally babbling, "I'm sorry for the inconvenience. So sorry."

"It will be my pleasure to get it," Michael replied as he grabbed me for the errand. At the liquor store Michael bought $200 worth of stuff. He even bought ice and some glasses.

Food was a long time coming and that really opened up the window of opportunity for a toast to Mexican Independence or whatever Cinco de Mayo stands for. Other guests were milling around, occasionally snatching crackers and sawing off corners of cheese from a 20-pound marble platter seemingly magically suspended on the clear glass coffee table. Bob asked "C" to pass him the cheese, and we all jerked toward the sharp sound when his wrist gave way and the marble cheese platter fell onto the glass-topped coffee table.

"Oh, my God. It's cracked," we all yelled (but couldn't be heard over the trumpets and guitars).

Michael reassured us, "I'm a decorator. I can fix this."

He magically moved magazines and candles around to cover the growing crack in the glass. With his flair and artistic decorating ability, it actually looked better than before the accident.

Hours passed and still no food, unless you count chips and dip. But there was more than enough to drink, so we proceeded to get plastered. In his attempt at being a good host, Raoul made the mistake of pointing out his favorite things, like his shell collection that was in a place of honor over the sofa. Hell, by then we couldn't tell a shell from a frijole, so we just nodded and smiled.

Old Bob Welch collapsed onto the sofa, forgetting that it didn't have a back and hit his head against Raoul's precious shelves. The next thing I saw was old Welch doing a complete back flip and his feet knocking the three-tiered contraption off the wall and sending the shells crashing to the floor. Some moments later, Bob untangled himself and peeked up over the overturned sofa, with a broken conch shell on his head.

Bob was very gracious and quickly tried to clean up the disaster, saying, "Oh my, I'm so terribly sorry. Let me write you a check to pay for this."

A visibly distraught Raoul replied, "Oh, no, no. Accidents happen. That's what friends are for. You just have to go with it, go with the flow." At this point, he was still just happy to have us there, but I could see a small tear in his eye.

At last, it was time for dinner and we were seated at a large table under the crucifix and surrounded by a 30-year-old plant that wove its way into a green frenzy as it climbed over the dining area archway. Raoul's mother had planted it the day he was born, he proudly announced. As hard as it had been, he had babied that heirloom vine wherever he had moved and I was given the seat of honor right under that tangled historical beast.

Kiln-fired Mexican bowls began their way around the table, each one mounded with loose stuff like beans, cheese, pasole, and rice. I had just passed a plate of tortillas to Bob when I saw, out of the corner of my eye, "C" spill his glass of wine.

With a dancer's quickness, I threw myself out of harm's way and, with the grace of a wobbling top; I spun out of control and into the plant. It was like a green monster had me; I was going down for the last time, but not without a fight. Within a few seconds it was over. The plant was uprooted, pulled off the wall, and dying around my feet. At least Jesus wasn't any worse for the wear.

Poor Raoul wasn't out of the woods yet. After he swept the green tangle into the corner, he rejoined us at the table. I had to feel sorry for the guy; he'd lost the bounce in his step. Of course, I felt terrible and kept on apologizing and offering to try to replace it (as if I could). Soon Raoul noticed that Bob hadn't eaten much at all and asked, "Is something wrong?"

Bob answered, "Oh, no, it's not that your food is not delectable to the palate; it's just your generous portions I could not consume."

We all looked at one another, did another check, and under his breath Steven said, "In other words, it tastes like shit."

Fortunately, no one heard the whispered insult and we ventured on without another hitch, until our exit, that is. As the party drew to a close, Raoul stood at the door and graciously said goodbye. I turned and looked back at the mess and was appalled at the devastation—the cracked coffee table, the broken shelves and shells, the destroyed plant; it looked like the Alamo, and the Mexicans lost.

As I walked out through the front door, I thanked Raoul for such a nice dinner, and my attention was grabbed by one last crisis. Steven's long narrow foot got caught in the stereo extension cord, and he nose-dived into the entertainment center, bringing it to a premature death. One good thing resulted, however, the god-awful music finally stopped. But wait, that wasn't all.

In the stunned silence, I became aware of the coat tree teetering back and forth as a result of Steven's impact, and before it could be righted, it fell into a painting and pierced the canvas as it tore it from the wall. There, that was all, the devastation was over and wasn't that enough?

We all groped for our checkbooks, but all Raoul could say was, "No, no, isn't that what friends are for? These are just material things. Friends just overlook things like this."

We drove away feeling terrible, yet starved. At a neck-breaking speed we caravaned to the Garden District to eat and to relive Cinco de Mayo. We were not without a conscience, however. Each of us sent Raoul a generous check and a lengthy apology for our "inconveniences." After all, that's what friends are for. The party had been an unparalleled disaster except for the fact that over the years it provided us with hours of laughter as we relived the story. I'm sure Davy Crockett smiled, too.

40

LANA

THERE IS MUCH TO LEARN IN LIFE, AND I DISCOVERED THAT THE most poignant lessons occurred unexpectedly while doing the most unremarkable things. As much of my maturation occurred in the privileged Beverly Hills community, I was educated in a distorted lifestyle of excess, yet inexplicably I was aware of matters of the heart and was sensitive to human longings and frailties. In the Beverly Hills mindset of achieving excellence through personal perfection, these frailties seemed magnified and inexcusable. After all, we had the time, money, and motivation to make every manageable aspect of our lives a "ten."

Take for instance the commonplace thought—"You ain't nothing unless you're rich, famous, or beautiful, or all three." To the majority of people, this is a discovery learned early on. Maybe it is learned in school where only the pretty cheerleaders and football heroes are heralded, or later in the local politics and economies of small towns and urban America where having wealth or the proper heritage places people at the top of the social ladder. I learned this lesson one afternoon while dining with Lana Turner.

While living in the penthouse in Century Park East, I became a good friend of Lana Turner's, who lived downstairs. This was long before she was on *Falcon Crest*, and no one had seen her for years. She had simply faded into the bleached blond version of a "Where's Waldo" poster along with the countless other aging actresses. One day she decided we should go to Jimmy's Restaurant for lunch.

Jimmy Murphy, once the maître d' at the Bistro, had opened up a great place right around the corner from Century Park East, and it had become one of my favorite places to go (partly because Brik had arranged for me to have a house account where I could just sign for anything I wanted). Because I ate at Jimmy's at least two times a week, I mistakenly assumed that Lana had been there, too.

The earliest, most glamorous Hollywood stars were given certain perks from the studios, and as part of her contract Lana had been provided a lifetime of limousine services to take her wherever she wanted to go. On that day she decided we needed its services, so she called up a limo to pick us up, even though Jimmy's was literally right around the corner.

She preceded me into the restaurant where Franco, the maître d', hugged and kissed me and made a big fuss. "We have your favorite table, Tony."

We were escorted through the bar to my favorite table, a banquette just a step down from the bar area that was bathed in the rich blues, greens, and golds Jimmy's was known for. As we approached our table, soft piano music warmed the moment and I was struck by Lana Turner's petite figure. She was probably only 5' tall.

I had noticed that they had cordially said "Hello" to Lana as we entered the restaurant, but it was a distant, "Who the hell are you?" greeting. They should have had enough clues such as the limo, the beautiful, expensive clothes, her impeccable grooming, and the elegant carriage of her head that, at every opportunity, glanced from side to side to see if anyone was impressed that she had arrived. No one was.

We were seated and Jimmy and his wife, Ann, personally greeted us again with a warm handshake and, for Lana, an inquisitive smile. They didn't recognize her at all; I could see that. I thought, my God, they don't realize that a legend is sitting in their restaurant for lunch and they're gushing and ooooohing over me. I was a nothing, except that I was sleeping with a star and hobnobbing with celebrities. It embarrassed and shocked me that a real Hollywood legend whose radiance had admittedly dimmed could so easily be forgotten. It was as if she had been parked away at Century Park East like a garaged Rolls-Royce or a closeted fine wine, never to be brought out for a sip or a spin.

A little bit later, I went to the men's room and passed Jimmy and Franco in the hall. They stopped me to ask, "Excuse me, Tony. Who is that you're with? She looks vaguely familiar."

"Vaguely familiar? That's Lana Turner, but don't make a big fuss now. She's going to know that it's nothing but bullshit."

As I returned to our table, I worried that our lighthearted luncheon had been unexpectedly spoiled, and I wanted to cover up for their ignorance and be able to reassure her that she had not withered and been forgotten. Nothing, I mean nothing, is worse for a Hollywood star than to be forgotten. Give them a car wreck, a kid on drugs, a dissed movie or two, but don't give them anonymity.

As I seated myself and returned the linen napkin to my lap, Lana gently took my hand in hers, looked deep into my eyes, and said knowingly, "You know, Tony, enjoy it now, enjoy the fleeting moment, because you're easily forgotten in this town."

Her beautiful, poignant smile showed resignation; she took it like a lady.

This brief incident with Lana Turner impressed upon me one of life's greatest lessons—"Enjoy the moment." So there in Jimmy's and with the legendary Lana Turner, I pondered a moment of discovery.

41

Snake

From the terrace of my penthouse I could see the lights of LAX and on a clear day even the tip of Catalina Island. This quickly became my favorite place to be. Expert gardening advice had helped me create a lush, green, private paradise right off the living room.

At first the pigeons were a delight, the rustle of wings, the sounds of nature, a discarded feather lying in the gardenias, ahhhh nature. The hunter green table and chairs were inviting, especially with a cup of coffee in the early morning hours. Unfortunately, the pigeons thought so, too. As a matter of fact, they enjoyed them too much.

One morning I was watering the plants, rearranging some, and reveling in the beautiful California sunrise when a paint-splatter hit my hand. I looked up to see what jerk was being careless on the roof, but there was no one to be seen. I noticed at once that the same sickly, whitish paint was splattered on the table and chairs, too. The more I looked, the more I discovered. My terrace looked like a Jackson Pollack painting during his intense period. As I walked in to wash up, I kept repeating, "Damn pigeons, damn fucking pigeons."

After a short investigation into bird and pest control, I bought a realistic rubber snake for the terrace. According to the experts, the oversized snake would completely deter the birds from the area. I had to admit that it did look real after I arranged it artfully slithering out of the vines that grew on the balcony railing. Wasn't it a bit outrageous to buy a snake as big as a boa constrictor to scare off a few pigeons? How stupid could they be? The pigeons and I had something in common; I forgot to tell Hattie.

Later that afternoon I came home from a luncheon and from the front door I looked out to the terrace and did a double take. Everything was broken up and tossed about. El Nino? Earthquake? The chairs were on their sides; the poor geraniums were depotted and barely clinging to life. So was Hattie.

Great cursing sobs greeted me as I rushed into the kitchen and saw Hattie, gasping for air, leaning up against the counter, and still armed with the broom.

"Tony! Tony! Thank God you're home."

"What? What the hell happened here, Hattie? Are you okay? Did someone break in?"

She pointed the broom towards the terrace. "He put up quite a fight, Tony, but I think he's dead," she panted with victorious pride in her voice.

"What are you talking about!?" I asked looking around for an dead intruder.

"I don't know how, but this big old snake got up here, and I beat the shit out of it with this broom. He stuck onto it, hissed at me; almost bit me twice. I swung it around and beat the shit out of him the best I could. I think he's dead now. Lord, Tony, what a day."

To make matters even worse, I laughed like hell and confessed, "Hattie, I forgot to tell you, that was a rubber snake. You dumb bitch!"

"WHAT? Bite me, white honky!" she screamed lunging at me with the broom.

It took quite a while for Hattie to laugh with me about that incident. It certainly wasn't that day, but after a few Jack Daniels, the two of us had the place pretty much back to normal. Hattie's blood pressure finally stabilized and as I escorted her out the door I glanced toward the terrace and saw a damn pigeon perched happily on the snake's head.

42

SCRAPS

OUR LIVES WERE NOT ALWAYS FILLED WITH TURMOIL OR ONE-upmanship. For the most part, we had a fun filled, loving relationship. But, to tell about cozy dinners or intimate talks on the phone aren't memorable or fun to hear about. My everyday life with Brik seemed to me as routine as a coalminer's...same hole...same shovel. I just waited for the next cave-in. (Okay, so the only dirt I got on my face was the mudpack treatment at La Costa Resort and Spa)

As the years passed, the indulgences of the fast lane began taking their toll on us. The paparazzi came sniffing around. Sometimes we had to change cars three times just to go to a restaurant or a play. I suppose it was the age old predicament: with notoriety came the loss of privacy. It was not knowing the future of our relationship as it struggled to exist in the heated up atmosphere that created unsettling overtones of concern for me. All that I'd known for years seemed in jeopardy now, or at least on shaky ground.

Once again after a minor altercation, over nothing basically, I felt the need to get even in my most creative way. My active imagination churned with solutions to this bump in the road.

As I watched Brik drive off to work that morning, I concocted the next chapter in our turbulent relationship. This time, however, instead of doing the move-out routine, I dreamed up a better retribution.

I got scissors and a bottle of wine and settled into a lawn chair on the balcony. The afternoon just flew by as I sliced and diced my way to a seamstress' nirvana as I hacked Brik's clothes into squares, triangles, and oblong swatches of expensive confetti. I timed the release event perfectly to coincide with Brik's return from the studios that evening. Just when I thought he would be arriving at the front door, I began the pleasurable act of dumping cut-up, quilt scrap-sized pieces of Brik's favorite $1,000 shirts over the balcony, setting them adrift on the light Pacific breezes. The silk pieces floated best. Maurice, the doorman, noticed them first.

When Brik stepped out of his car and gave the keys to the valet, he noticed several of the doormen staring up into space, distracted from their duties.

Maurice commented to Brik as he walked toward the front door, "Some woman must have gone crazy because she's ripping up her man's clothes."

The source of the craziness couldn't be determined because of the wind and distance to the 21st floor. However, I found out later that Brik recognized a piece of one of his favorite shirts that came to rest on the landscaping right in front of him. I could hear him screaming and laughing long before he opened the door to my penthouse. He said as he grabbed me in his arms, "Everyone thinks that some woman went crazy and is ripping up her husband's clothes."

I said, "Well?"

My anger long gone now, I could laugh with him. Sometimes therapy can be very expensive, I mused.

43

BEDFORD

THE PENTHOUSE PROVIDED ME WITH A COMFORTABLE PLUSH HAVEN for over six years. The conveniences, amenities, and friends I met there couldn't be matched and except for the lack of privacy, it was perfect.

Privacy wasn't a particular concern for me, but it was for Brik. As far as the public knew, he was a perfect example of American manhood with a gorgeous wife and a very high-profile acting career. His television hit churned out countless episodes and his star rose meteorically during those years. With his increasingly high profile came intensified public curiosity. Life at Century Park East was anything but private and the staff relished inside gossip; many times sharing it with the tabloids.

At the penthouse, phone calls were answered by an answering service, and because of the valet parking, all excursions were observed. The arrival and departure of guests revolved around answering the security check when they arrived and then calling the valet to retrieve the guest's vehicle at the end of their visit. Of course, Brik had his own parking space, but all of the staff knew that he lived there some of the time.

As I mentioned before, the paparazzi were beginning to get wind of our arrangement, and that created tentative, suspicious feelings and anxieties.

To outside observers every facet of Brik's life was like a storybook, but I was a hidden chapter to be kept under lock and key and away from public scrutiny. Hollywood tended to protect the stars, and for the most part it protected the Brik Moor III who loved another man, but many times money talked and could turn the head of those who had the keys to the hidden chapters. We began to sense an urgency to move from Century Park East to protect his future. It was time for me to have my own house.

Brik came home one night and announced that he had a house in Beverly Hills for me to see. It was right before Thanksgiving in 1979 when I first saw the North Bedford house located in the prestigious area known as the flats of Beverly Hills between Santa Monica and Sunset Boulevards. No convincing was necessary as far as I was concerned because it was wonderful.

North Bedford Drive was in an older, exclusive section of Beverly Hills known for its Hollywood history and convenient location to shopping and cultural perks. We drove up to a two-story, Spanish-style house with a tile roof and beautiful landscaping. The doorways were arched and the backyard was a pleasure with its flagstone paths that wound through lush plants draped on painted trellises and dense flowering bushes from which colorful birds appeared and disappeared. There was a fountain and even a small area for a garden that I later made good use of. No need to look any further, I commented.

We placed the penthouse on the market and quickly sold it for a substantial sum. Brik kindly gave me the $300,000 profit. His generosity, however, didn't end there; he also presented me with a new car and the first of nine summers in the South of France. Some house-warming gifts, huh?

Of course, the new house required new furnishings. The contemporary chrome, mirrors, yellows, and browns from the penthouse weren't appropriate for the warm and traditional Bedford house, so I started from scratch and bought everything from canopy beds to Queen Anne wing-backed chairs.

I hardly knew where I preferred to be in the house because every room was inviting and comfortable—we had dark Thomasville wood furniture and tapestry-covered sofas. Nestled in the quiet darkness were treasures of Lalique crystal that I loved to back-light on the rich wood display shelves.

I mentioned a new car. Brik surprised me with a beautiful, yellow El Dorado, complete with a creamy leather interior; sunroof; and tape system. I treated passing motorists to the pulsating sounds of the disco version of Evita. Many times Rex, Sonny, Wayne, and I would cruise around jiving to its repetitious beat, the sunroof open to the California sun.

"Don't cry for me, Argentina!" we'd scream.

I would take the corners with a flair and delighted in watching in the rear view mirror as the guys slid across the leather seats and howled complaints of mistreatment. Of course, with the music so loud, I only saw two gaping mouths open and assumed they were shouting words of encouragement. Those were the days.

44

TITTIES

THE NORTH BEDFORD HOUSE GAVE US THE PRIVACY WE WERE looking for. We were able to conduct our lives away from the scrutiny of others. Hattie was with me full-time there and in my mind, it was Hattie's home as much as mine because she was my constant companion, my defense against loneliness.

Over the months, and after all the fixing up was completed, she relaxed into the role of the woman of the house. Sometimes in the late afternoon we would drink a little bourbon and coke together and watch wrestling on television. Actually, she watched the wrestling and I watched her. She would sit on the edge of the ottoman, leaning toward the set, swearing, cheering, and threatening anyone who was dishonorable. How I loved her temper, her spark; she was my entertainment, my constant, my love. She revealed herself to me and allowed me to do the same.

After a time, she shed herself of those uncomfortable grooming accessories such as teeth and bras. These were brought to her attention one morning when Brik gave orders for the dinner party he had planned for that evening. He had a bug up his ass and ranted on and on about his expectations for the party. He didn't want her drinking; she was to wear her teeth and a uniform complete with a starched cap. I heard the reprimand and cringed because I knew Hattie would get even some way. I braced for the retribution.

Our guests, two gay couples from the studio, arrived that evening and immediately commented on the luscious smells coming from the kitchen. Hattie had prepared beautiful appetizers and a wine and chicken dish that would have pleased a king. We enjoyed a cocktail before dinner and eventually drifted towards the dining room and seated ourselves under another Waterford chandelier.

As I adjusted my chair under the table, I heard a familiar tune drifting from the kitchen and cringed.

"Oh, when I was young and in my prime,
I could get me a lay most any time.
But now I'm old and my puss's cold,
and I can't get me a lay to save my soul."

Chills of anticipation drowned me. I prepared myself for a show. Hattie's bare, snaggy hammer-toes glided across the Persian rugs, but no one saw them. Nor did anyone notice the gleaming silver tray bearing the white wine and chicken main course that she brought in, nor her soft humming. People did notice, however, her enormous titties unsuccessfully hidden behind a sheer black negligee.

She walked toward Brik, her unfettered jugs swaying over the meal. After the tittie shock, one noticed her shiny toothless gums and then her "Bride of Frankenstein" ratted up hairdo crowned with a paper cap. It was a lot to take in all at once. With a purposeful glint in her steely eyes and a slight waft of bourbon, Hattie sidled up to Brik and extended her bare, jiggling arms outright, offering him the silver dish and said, "May I helps you, sir?" Brik almost jumped out the window.

Let it be known that, after that night, Brik never gave her rude orders again. Point well made, I thought, because Hattie was a loyal employee who could have exposed our affair, and cashed in on it. Instead, she was a true confidant and remains an honorable, cherished friend to this day.

45

RICH

MY MEMORIES OF LIVING IN THE NORTH BEDFORD HOUSE ARE rich with laughter and friends. While I was there, I met a wide variety of people who became an integral part of my extended family. There were many gay friends, but my family circle also included several sets of heterosexual couples. One common bond we all shared was that we knew how to laugh and have fun. Another thing we shared was our access to money which allowed us to travel, party, and play together.

I met Jan and Robert Myles and Sandra and Max Spaulding from New York who were very much on the sophisticated social schedule of the rich. The Spaulding's routine included taking vacations in the Hamptons and Monaco where they were close friends with Princess Grace and Prince Rainier. Both couples derived their enormous wealth from famous clothing lines that supplied them with seemingly limitless opportunities. It was through my association with these couples and their friends that I was exposed to another facet of the diamond of life.

I remember being in Jan Myles' dressing area one afternoon as she got ready for dinner. The impressive room was about 25' by 25', complete with Jacuzzi tub, and adjacent to this room was her walk-in closet, dripping with expensive clothes, and even larger than her dressing room. It was kind of like Imelda Marcos' closet, only with a new-world appeal. Not many glittering crowns and such, just shelves, drawers, and nooks and crannies of unique, color-coded outfits. Some architect must have had a ball concocting this clever storage area that resembled a marriage of Frank Lloyd Wright and Rube Goldberg inventions.

Had I been interested, I would have watched Jan emerge from the tub, but I was so blown away by her closet I spent those minutes trying to memorize the extent of her kingdom of clothing. Naturally, clothes, shoes, coats, and accessories were compartmentalized; jeans were hanging together (designer versus lesser designer, etc.); there were clever pullout drawers with shiny glass fronts for each pair of shoes; and whole collections of feathery boas gently moved near the scarf section and before the cedar-lined fur storage. I felt as if I was in a tightly organized Neiman Marcus store, only the tags had been removed.

These were the days of promiscuity, and modesty was unheard of, so it was common for me to perch on one of the gold tapestry stools and watch her put on her makeup, her bare arms extended out of a plush towel that she had loosely wrapped around her. We would sip champagne, laugh, and decide what she would wear that evening. I'll never forget some words she spoke to me that day as she blotted her face with a fresh towel and dropped it to the thick white carpet near the dressing table.

Rather appalled, I said, "Jan, what are you doing? Why did you just drop the towel to the floor?"

She replied, "You see how quickly you become a slob when you have someone picking up after you." Those words came back to haunt me years later when I had a staff of four and found myself doing the same thing.

Jan and Robert Myles were awash with "new" money, and we were all genuinely happy for them, celebrating every new major purchase with toasts and cheers. They had a Rolls-Royce, a Mercedes, and later, a chauffeur-driven limousine. Jan worked in the clothing business alongside Robert, so it was decided that she needed the limousine to be comfortable during her daily commute. The first time we climbed into the cavernous limo, with its wall-to-wall black leather upholstery, we twisted around, exploring every drawer, knob, and convenience. We had the driver raise the privacy window and then we screamed like excited kids. We examined and played with everything— the two televisions, the VCRs, liquor cabinet, and tape system. Everyone really rooted for each other's success and nothing was taken for granted.

Another fond memory of Jan occurred one afternoon as she prepared the dining room table for company. She was working with a house servant named Fatima who asked her what serviettes should she set for the luncheon. I saw a blank look on Jan's face. Fatima repeated her question, and again she got a blank expression from Jan.

I moved behind Jan and whispered, "Napkins, fool."

"Pink, please," she replied.

When Fatima walked to the kitchen, Jan turned to me, "Isn't that something? My help's got more class than me."

For several years my life was deeply involved with the Spauldings and the Myles. Fueled by laughter, alcohol, and cocaine we lived in a whirlwind, nonstop party. I'm not sure if we were actually addicted to the drugs or alcohol, but they became a constant presence, and I know we became addicted to the hilarious laughter that spiced our adventures.

Several other couples joined us in our fun, but it was the Spauldings and the Myles who were my fast, constant, and closest friends. The Spauldings became known as the "New York" contingent and would come to Los Angeles to party at least ten days a month. In return, the Myles and I would fly to New York for at least ten days a month, too. Brik would frequently fly in for a few days to join us, but his schedule was governed by his work at the studio, his wife, and his straight life. Besides, he knew that I was in safe hands and having a marvelous time with my friends.

The bimonthly commute between Los Angeles and New York was by no means a drudgery because we flew the airline known as Regent Air, which later became known as MGM Grand. It catered to the rich and famous with its pricey tickets and red carpet service.

I would phone in a reservation, and if it was to be a short trip I'd tell Hattie to pack for me. For extended excursions, I had a packing service come to the house to arrange and pack my clothes into hanging wardrobe boxes. After some instruction as to which particular colors or styles I wanted, they would arrange my garments into color-coordinated ensembles, complete with belts, socks, ties, and scarves.

Everything was done for me. A limousine would pick me up and take me to a private area of the airport that literally rolled out the red carpet and provided its customers with a private, secluded gate. During the limo ride from home to the airport, I would sip champagne provided by the airline. I never saw my luggage again after I left home because it was moved about with military precision from the house to the plane to the limo at destination and then to our apartment in New York at the Plaza 400 building. There was never a wait at the airport because everything was timed to the minute in order to provide convenience to those people who could afford to have the best.

I believe the jet was a 737 that had been remodeled to accommodate 30 passengers. The coast-to-coast, five-hour flight was delightful because the plane had a chef, a masseuse, a manicurist, hairdressers, over-stuffed seats with individual video tapes, conference rooms, and private suites for sleeping or whatever. The bar and conference areas of the plane were divided by exquisite Lalique glass panels. Needless to say, flying was a delight on Regent Air.

In Manhattan, Brik and I had an apartment near Sutton Place and a chauffeur-driven limousine at our disposal. We spent hours shopping, going to plays, and dining at the finest restaurants. The night was never over after a fine meal and a play. We would party on at "after hours" bars until 4:30 or 5:00 a.m.

It was natural that I cultivated expensive tastes. My clothing bills alone rose to thousands of dollars a month. My personal shopper at Neiman Marcus in Beverly Hills was a sweetheart and kept me informed of the new arrivals of exclusive, one-of-a-kind items from Versace, Thierry Mugler from Paris, or Kansai from the Orient. Gina's ratted up black hair, short skirts, and six-inch fingernails made her look like a character from Asian mythology. She dialed the phone with her knuckles because these nails got in the way. The weapon-like fingernails really captivated my imagination. I always imagined that she lived a wild life until I unexpectedly ran into her in a Beverly Hills restaurant. That evening I was robbed of my fantasy of Gina being a promiscuous lady because she introduced me to her husband of 25 years and two of her grown children. Gina kept me in the height of fashion for years and remains a friend to this day.

According to most people's needs, my clothing collection was excessive, but because I socialized every day and night within a wealthy, prominent circle of friends, I had to be appropriately dressed. Brik approved of my newly acquired, expensive tastes because he felt that they were a reflection of his style and ability to provide for me.

I needed several tuxedos for the most formal events, but when dining out in Beverly Hills during the 70s and 80s, it was very stylish for men to wear outfits that included a tuxedo shirt, a Versace jacket, jeans or leather pants with a Keiselstein-Cord belt, and Tony Lama boots. Jean Paul Gaultier shirts with their back tab were popular then, as well as Calvin Klein underwear. For an afternoon of drinking and socializing, many times I wore a low-cut, pastel Calvin Klein undershirt under a cropped Kansai jacket, and, if the weather warranted, I enjoyed pulling out one of my favorite furs from Stompers in Beverly Hills. For nightwear, I wore silk boxers with dashing, luxurious robes by Fernando Sanchez, which pleased Brik greatly.

To enhance my exquisite wardrobe, I kept a deep tan and a trim, fit body that I honed during my daily sessions with Jane Fonda at 6:30 a.m. and Richard Simmons at 7:30 a.m. In a way, I was a showpiece for Brik, so when we went to openings and events such as the Emmys and the Oscars, it was expected that I look great.

46

AEROBICS

A TYPICAL BEVERLY HILLS DAY WENT SOMETHING LIKE THIS—AT
6:00 a.m. I dressed to sweat and drove to Jane Fonda's
6:30 a.m. exercise class at her studio called "Jane Fonda's
Workout" on Robertson Boulevard. She was perfection in
motion; with a lean vitality and nonstop, almost brutal energy.

The studio was sparse: the typical walls of mirrors reflected
the unfilled dreams of the models, housewives, and starlets who
religiously leaped to a count and kicked on call. With a drill
sergeant's authority, Jane would bark out the routines over the
pulsing music, and we tried to please her, ever striving to grimace
less and stay synchronized with her every move. She was in
magnificent condition, always upbeat.

At the end of the workout, during the cool-down, we could
no longer focus on our exhausted bodies in the mirrors because
sweat was pouring off our hair, faces, and every other part of
our bodies. The last thing I'd see as I left Jane's class was a
worker pushing a wide mop across the wet exercise floor. With
as much composure as I could muster, I would force a jaunty
bounce in my step and throw up a hand to say "goodbye" to

her. Her thin arm would rise from her posture perfect body, and she would wiggle her fingers, "see you tomorrow."

Feeling like I'd just been part of the Normandy invasion, I would drive the Mercedes to Richard Simmon's studio and salad bar known as "The Ruffage," located on little Santa Monica Boulevard. It was a small establishment with a tiny eating area and a single exercise room in the back. Taped disco music and Richard's bantering welcomed his "victims." Richard's faithful included many television and movie stars. During the years I exercised there, I sweated with some of the best of them, from the cast of General Hospital to Richie Cunningham's mother.

The people in Richard's classes had a lot to overcome. They had to drive by the Wonder Bread Company and smell the heavenly aroma of baking bread on their way to class. He would yell, "Forget about the bread." But the smells would permeate the walls and windows of the studio and beckon our weakened wills with a devilish reminder of what normal Americans were doing at 7:30 a.m. in the morning. During the next hour, Donna Summers' top disco hits propelled us onward, and the frenetic Richard implored us to scale new heights of dedicated exercising.

I was actually intiminated by Richard Simmons and after gaining three or four pounds on a trip, I would starve myself before going back to his class.

But, people sensed he was genuinely rooting for them and he had some emotional stake in their health. He was a whirlwind of emotion and an amazingly entertaining soul who touched people and, for many, he really made a difference in their size and self-esteem. (And even today, he stays on his path of making dreams come true with knocking out walls to rescue an obese soul, or dealing cards to learn nutrition, or organizing a Sweating to the Oldies Cruise. God bless you, Richard.)

At the end of his class, which in many ways was even harder than Jane Fonda's, he would share an inspirational, "Now, let's go out and get 'em" speech. I'd leave choked with emotional determination. Yes! Today I'd get those servants busy cleaning the chandeliers.

47

CHOIR

AFTER THE WORKOUTS, MANY TIMES I WENT FOR JUICE WITH FRIENDS
and then home to give the servants instructions for their chores
for the day. The big decision was whether or not to go to
lunch with friends or to go shopping, or both. The days went
by quite quickly.

Not every moment was self-centered, however. As a result
of meeting Loretta Young, I got involved with charity work at
the Good Shepherd Church in Beverly Hills and donated time
to their "feeding the homeless" program.

Loretta Young is a staunch Catholic who went to mass every
day at the Good Shepherd. I met her one day because I was
singing "How Great Thou Art" behind her in church when
she turned around, cupped my face in her hands, and said,
"Today, I heard an angel sing."

Here was a beautiful movie star legend who typified what
the old movie stars were really like, telling me that I sang like an
angel. She was one of the people with whom I instantly fell in
love.

She was the one who encouraged me to join the choir at
the Good Shepherd where we were directed by June, a prima

donna spinster (an Edna Mae Oliver look-a-like) choir leader. The choir consisted of ordinary people just wanting to sing for the Lord, but June acted as if we were the Boston Pops and the Mormon Tabernacle Choir all rolled up into one.

In my mind, she was too serious and strict. One of her rules was to enter the choir room with a respectful and quiet demeanor. When she entered the room, all rustling and talking stopped because she had begun implementing a demerit system that punished troublemakers. Heaven help us if we didn't obey her every gesture and command, or if we bent down the corner of a page in our hymnal.

June was as high-strung as a power line and just loved it if we got something wrong so she could show us the "right" way it should be performed.

She'd say, "Now, here's how the song should be sung."

Then, her virgin bosom rising and falling with each verse and her thin red lips stretched to Texas, she would sing the song with exaggerated vibrato and enunciation. Of course, the entire choir would stand and clap in appreciation for being enlightened and also to suck up. With fake modesty, she would clap her hands and say, "Now, now, I know you can do as well. Once again, with feeling." I could tell that she was rooting for mistakes.

We'd barely knock out another line or two when her frantic hands would wave us to a rude halt.

"NO, NO! Too much overlapping. Sing it this way." (If you can, you yokels.) She'd nod her dark, sprayed hairdo at the organist, and demonstrate again. Our choir sessions consisted of about ten minutes of singing and an hour of listening to her correct our "mistakes."

One Sunday morning the choir performed "You'll Never Walk Alone," and as our voices slowed to a stop, the congregation rose as one to applaud their heartfelt appreciation. June turned to the cheering audience, raised her robe-covered arms, and bowed grandly as if she were at Carnegie Hall. Her skinny leg kicked at the front of her robe to show a spinster's idea of a fashionable shoe, and she bowed low like Prince Charming presenting his new bride. She basked in the glory of the moment. That was embarrassing enough, but when I saw a large lace handkerchief clutched in her right hand, I realized the ugly truth...June wanted to be Luciano Pavarotti.

48

HOMELESS

BACK TO LORETTA YOUNG. ONE OF THE CHARITIES SHE GOT US involved in was feeding the homeless. Our perception of ourselves as "do-gooders" now seems misguided at best. I suppose drugs really warped my view of reality. We would arrive at the West Hollywood Park in our Rolls-Royces and Mercedes, gingerly step around dirt traps waiting for our Gucci loafers, arch our backs, and scan the horizon desperately seeking a familiar face. It was us against them (the haves and the have-nots, the ashamed and the no-shames).

The homeless would queue up and begin shuffling down the food line never looking up or saying much. Too bad—if they had talked, they would have been spared hearing our animated conversations as we slapped mush out of soup tureens onto the assembly line of plates that were handed from one manicured hand to another.

As the homeless trudged by on the other side of the table, they would hear things like, "Oh, last night we went to the Polo Lounge."

"We went to Mortons. You know what? That veal chop was a bit spongy."

"My champagne was flat."

After serving the meal, we would slide onto luxurious leather seats, flip on the air conditioner, turn on the latest disco hit, and head for home feeling euphorically happy for having volunteered our time. Yeah, right, like we had something better to do. We weren't needed in surgery and didn't need to wash windows. All of us went on and on about our small disappointments in front of the poor homeless who had nothing.

We were serving these poor people and didn't have a clue. Why didn't we have them come to the church hall to be fed, and why didn't we dress down? What were we thinking? How twisted was that? Not one of us had a glimpse of reality. Forgive me. Now I know better.

49

VACATIONS

IN THE EARLY 1980s WE BEGAN ANOTHER BIRTHDAY TRADITION; my 4th of July birthday was celebrated in Monte Carlo. For nine years my friends and I flew on the Concorde and languished for six weeks in the seductive South of France. As our annual trips drew near, we never excitedly called one another with new sightseeing suggestions. We were concerned with more immediate things, such as selecting our new wardrobes and accessories, and making arrangements for our cocaine supplies to be shipped to our destinations. You see, we weren't traveling to the South of France to saturate our senses or stimulate our minds—we went to enjoy ourselves. We were simply moving our party east...thousands of miles east.

Usually Hattie packed my things for the extended summer vacation. Over a period of days, she would carefully lay out expensive, color coordinated outfits, always checking every detail for "her boy." My jewelry was packed in a Louis Vuitton duffel bag that I hand-carried onto the Concorde. I favored the Armani and Versace clothing lines and Hattie made sure each was well represented. The wardrobe she packed included tuxedos and beautiful tailored suits that were appropriate for the most exclusive affairs. And as for beach wear, we let Mother Nature take care of that.

Hattie definitely had me covered. Actually, some of me was covered. For casual day wear and shopping strolls, I brought skimpy chammy shorts with laced-up sides and matching low-cut buckskin shirts and jackets from North Beach Leather and International Male. My favorite outfits were the leather jumpsuits with full-length zippers that allowed me to adjust the view for admirers. I got used to being followed by French crowds who thought that I was an American movie star. Each year I selected outfits that would continue that illusion.

The Myles, and I would fly Regent Air to New York a few days before leaving for France because we wanted to see a couple of the new Broadway shows and catch up with friends. From New York, we boarded the Concorde for the awesome three-plus-hour trip to Paris. As jaded as I became living the luxurious Beverly Hills life, the Concorde flights never became mundane to me.

Just viewing the Concorde on the J.F.K. runway was a thrill. The crooked-necked, rather small plane was a universally recognized symbol of luxury, but I flew the Concorde because it was fast. I was a horrible flying traveler and I really only got through it with the help of Valium and champagne. Taking the Concorde meant relief from the countless hours required by regular transatlantic flights.

We had our cocaine shipped to us at each city, but I was the one who brought along our "traveling" supply. I slipped several days worth of cocaine in my sock and then slid on my Tony Lama boots. I never even gave it a thought that I could be caught with drugs in a foreign country, or even my country either. It never occurred to me that I might be starring in a real version of "Midnight Express."

The Concorde was not spacious, just a rather narrow aisle
with double matching passenger seats on either side. Its signature, nearly vertical take-offs and landings were unique in all
the world of flying. On the wall in front of the passengers was
a speed gauge that was watched by all with zombie-like trances
as the plane reached and exceeded the speed of sound. Before
reaching the speed of sound, it shuddered and was noisy, but
we didn't care, because it was our rocket to France.

I can only estimate the cost of our six-week summer vacations, but each easily topped $50,000 dollars. The Myles,
Spauldings, and I were a traveling party that sometimes absorbed other friends for a few days. Brik came when he could
get away from his wife and the studio, but he was never able to
be with us for the entire six-week stay.

After landing in Paris, we caught a flight to Nice, and from
there we motored to Monte Carlo where we checked into the
grand Hotel de Paris. The old world elegance graciously welcomed us and from my balcony I could see the lights of the
Palace of Monaco. I fondly remember the nights in Monte
Carlo. Sometimes we would dine outside and the cool Mediterranean breezes would flutter the linen tablecloths and softly
ruffle the flowing dresses of my beautiful lady friends. We
could sip French wine and watch well-dressed strollers making
their way to the casino. Sometime we would drive 35 miles to
La Reserve Restaurant where we could dine on the terrace and
watch the magical lights of Monaco at night.

Usually, after dinner, we would carouse and dance the night
away at places like Jimmy's and Regine's. We would sleep in
until 11:00 a.m. or 12:00 noon in the mornings and then re-
group for a day of shopping and dining. When we were exhausted from that, we would lie naked on the beaches or take
saunas or get massages. Time passed very pleasantly in Monte

Carlo. The cloak of Americanism, the stigma of being visitors from the United States, began to drop from our shoulders. The European attitude and sense of time and class became ours as we rested up for our weeks in St. Tropez.

Hotel Byblos, in St. Tropez, was our Mediterranean paradise-home for the second part of our vacation. Small patios and courtyards were surrounded with lavender and olive trees. The beaches were minutes away and the ocean breezes stirred the pungent air. As fashionable as Hotel Byblos was, it was just a launching spot for us.

St. Tropez is a unique combination of modern freedoms and its thousand-year-old past. We walked the cobblestone streets in town and enjoyed the seafood restaurants hidden down winding side-streets in the fishing village. But this was not a sleepy, old-fashioned town.

This was the place to party, and party we did. We always celebrated Sandra Spaulding's birthday with a day on the beach at Club 55 and then partied the night away at La Cave, just below the Byblos. Jacquelyn, the proprietor at La Cave, welcomed many famous celebrities to her exclusive club. People danced on the small tables and were secretly impressed with the fabulous decor that included waterfalls tumbling behind glass walls.

Inhibitions weren't allowed in St. Tropez. We left ours on the Concorde. Once, we were shopping in a small store for thongs. I selected one I wished to try on, but they just laughed when I asked directions to the dressing room. "Just drop your pants and try it on. What difference does it make?" they said. I had to agree with that logic and took their suggestion.

It was here that I was especially watched and followed. Crowds would gather and follow me about as I shopped or strolled the streets of St. Tropez. We all dressed to kill and I definitely did my share of killing. Wherever I went I drew whistles, smiles, and comments. At the gay club, La Pigeonaire, I dazzled everyone. Sophie, the owner of La Pigeonaire, introduced me to everyone as if I was a famous star. I remember thinking, as I lay on the beaches of St. Tropez basking in the sun and all the attention, that I'd better enjoy the moment, because it was all downhill from there. We would pick up FedEx packages of cocaine shipments at the hotel and there never was a hitch. Then, of course, we never thought that there would be.

Several times we rented a yacht and sailed to the Hotel du Cap Eden Roc where we stayed for a few days. There we enjoyed a magnificent pool that was formed in a blasted crevice in the terraced cliffs overlooking the Mediterranean Sea. The restaurant was cantilevered out over the cliffs and the deep blue water below. The costs were fairly typical here: $8.00 to tip for a bucket of ice, $35.00 for a dry-cleaned shirt. They didn't take credit cards, just cash or traveler's checks.

After a decadent two weeks in St. Tropez, we would retire to Paris and the Plaza Athenee Hotel where we had our own butler and maid. Each room was a step back into the times of Louis XIV with ornate antiques and fireplaces. At dinner we were soothed with piano and violin music, slowly bringing us back to civilization after the wildness of St. Tropez. Here we rested, ate, and shopped until it was time to fly the Concorde back to New York, where I always stayed another two weeks visiting family and friends before flying Regent Air back to Beverly Hills. With small variations, this became our yearly vacation for nine summers.

50

LIZ

IN THE EARLY 1980S, THE NEW YORK CONTINGENT FLEW IN WITH a special goal in mind, to see Elizabeth Taylor in the opening night of *Little Foxes*. The "after" party was at La Cage aux Folles. Brik and I gathered our friends, the Spauldings, Myles, and Glynns, around our usual table in the front and slightly to the left of center stage. Spirits were high after the soaring performances and excitement of the opening night of *Little Foxes*. By the time we arrived at La Cage, we were all on our way to being rip-roaring drunk. (Additionally, we had enjoyed some hits of cocaine to bolster our carefree mood.)

Two tables away from us sat the enchanting Elizabeth Taylor, who was at times completely surrounded by friends and acquaintances. I could not keep my eyes off her, nor could anyone else. Her magnetic attraction captured the curious, and they orbited, if not in body, at least visually, within her gravitational pull. Even the famous glanced her way hoping to observe the emotions and reactions reflected in her stunning, violet eyes. I was one of those.

Rock Hudson, Zsa Zsa Gabor, and Merv Griffin were her table companions. Thanks to the champagne and cocaine, my condition had deteriorated into an extreme state of over-confidence. Unexpectedly, I found myself advancing toward Elizabeth's table on a mission to introduce myself to someone who obviously would want to meet me, too. Oh, the delusions of drugs.

What could have and should have been my most embarrassing moment turned into a cherished memory. It was electric just standing by Elizabeth Taylor's side as she spoke with a woman who had broken through the protective private circle of friends that surrounded her. The intruder told Elizabeth that she was cousins with one of her ex-husbands. The violet eyes briefly clouded over, and dimmed a bit, but she plowed on with the unpleasant conversation and commented, "Oh really? Who?"

"Eddie Fisher."

She abruptly turned toward me, rose from her chair, and took my arm saying that she was just about to have a bottle of champagne with this handsome young gentleman. The woman's mouth gaped open as I escorted Elizabeth Taylor toward our table.

The first thing I said to her was, "Isn't the world full of assholes? As we maneuvered across the floor, I introduced myself, but she mentioned that she knew who I was and that Rock had spoken of me.

"Yes," I answered. Brik and I were close friends with Rock Hudson and she quickly grasped our relationship. For the next hour, I had the ultimate pleasure of sipping expensive champagne with the world's premier movie star, Elizabeth Taylor. We laughed at the people around us and easily chatted about the premiere. As we polished off the last of the Dom

Perignon, I took a mental photo of this beautiful, complex woman. We stood up to return to our tables, and she bussed my cheek. See, I knew she wanted to meet me.

I couldn't wait to call Mom the next morning and tell her that I met Elizabeth Taylor, and, just as I suspected, the first thing she asked me was, "What did you talk about?"

"Isn't the world full of assholes?" I replied.

Elizabeth and I became good friends and had some great times. We partied together and even went to Malcolm Forbes' New Jersey Estate for his Christmas party.

One Christmas, I flew into New Jersey to go to Malcolm Forbes' Christmas party and enjoyed a dinner out at Tulapano's Restaurant with my folks several nights before the big extravaganza. People at the surrounding tables heard that I was going to the Forbes' big bash and seemed in awe of me.

Eventually a woman came up to me with bulging, curious eyes wanting to know what it was like at Malcolm Forbes' parties. She asked if caviar was piled high everywhere and if only the best champagne was served.

I said, "What? The night we go there, the night before the party, everyone is hanging around in sweats. No caviar then, it's much more likely you'd be slugging down a beer, and Elizabeth Taylor will throw you the can of peanuts."

I would have been wasting my breath to further destroy her mind full of misconceptions by also adding that the gorgeous movie icon was even prettier on the inside than on the outside, and that even though Elizabeth's beauty had brought her endless attention, it could overwhelm aquaintances and distance her from many of life's ordinary pleasures—that would have simply been too much to take.

51

JULES

A DEAR FRIEND, JULIE BOYCE, GAVE US AN UNNEEDED EXCUSE TO
fly to New York. Her birthday was, however, reason enough
to heighten everyone's expectations for a fabulous ten days in
the Big Apple. Jules was absolutely gorgeous, but then all the
women in our group were. How many times need I say the
word "beautiful" when describing the women in our close
group? They were all blessed with a classy, enviable beauty.

Of course, it also helps to have money. Jules, like Jan and
the others, wore expensive gowns by Fabrice, Bob Mackie, and
Nolan Miller. Madison Avenue's Harry Winston and Fred
Leighton were their sources for the glittering jewelry that created
the final dramatic touches for an evening out. They were all on
a first-name basis with the most prominent fashion designers.
Money talks.

Jules and her husband Terry derived their wealth from the
toy industry. Their company raked in untold millions of dollars
from its worldwide distribution and manufacturing endeavors.
But she was not just blessed with money and beauty; she was a
wit of monumental proportions.

One day several of us decided to call Jules to meet us for an impromptu lunch. From Sandra's magnificent apartment overlooking the river and the 59th Street bridge, I dialed Jules and found myself talking to her maid, Sadie, who told me that Mrs. Boyce was at a wedding. But before we left for lunch, the phone rang, and it was Jules.

Surprised, I said, "I thought you were at a wedding."

"Oh, my dear, I was," she purred. "I looked stunning, too, in my light blue, beaded Fabrice gown."

"But, Jules, that's too formal for this hour," I anguished.

"No, dear, not when it's a wedding on All My Children. I'll change and meet you at lunch in 30 minutes."

I covered the mouthpiece of the phone, laughing, and reported to the others, "She had dressed up to watch a wedding on All My Children, but she's coming to lunch with us." If televisions could talk, I thought.

After dining at Le Cirque and partying, Jules, Terry, Brik, and I landed at a pissy French club named Tout de Suite, a famous "after hours" club. Even at 3:00 and 4:00 a.m. the place was crowded. Flashing neon lights reflected from the rows of shiny limousines that were lined up around the block near Tout de Suite. A light rain was falling as we bent under large umbrellas held by our chauffeurs and ducked into the seedy door to the club. The patrons partied on through the night knowing that some poor, weary driver would whisk them home, even occasionally having to carry them to their bed.

The Boyces had recently employed a new chauffeur, providing him with a secure job and a gun under the front seat for protection. Jules was the stunning one of the group that evening in a black, high-necked Bob Mackie gown that dropped dangerously low in the back to reveal three-tiered strands of diamonds, each ending with large marble-sized ruby baubles.

Total carats? Probably thirty, including the rubies. Naturally, the necklaces were properly balanced with diamond rings and earrings. I'd say we were blinded by about $300,000 worth of jewels that evening. Before riding the creaking elevator up to the bar, we cautioned Julie about her jewelry.

"Oh, it wouldn't be wise to wear all of that in there, would it, Jules?"

"Oh, I suppose you're right," she admitted.

She removed all of her jewels, except her wedding ring, and dropped them into a crumpled up paper sack she found under the armrest in the back of the limo. She rolled down the bag into a nondescript, sandwich-sized package, lay it on the seat, and tootled her fingers toward the chauffeur as we walked into the front door. Brik and I looked knowingly at one another as we followed the Boyces into Touts.

Hours (probably seconds) later, the limousine, driver, gun, and jewels had dissolved into the surreal New York night. When we finally called it a night, the Boyces' ride was long gone. No ride, no jewels, no surprise. However, this did not cause major turmoil for the Boyces because, after hailing a cab, they merely called Lloyd's of London to begin the insurance claim procedures for reimbursement of the stolen jewels. It was, after all, just a matter of money.

A favorite place to have cocktails and do coke in New York was at the cocktail lounge in the Sherry-Netherland Hotel located at the corner of 59th and Fifth Avenue. Our group spent many evenings drinking, laughing, and enjoying lines of cocaine in its dark, inviting elegance. We would sit there for hours, occasionally ordering something to eat, like a huge bowl of crab and shrimp served over ice in a crystal bowl. With appetites diminished and dulled by the cocaine and alcohol, very little was eaten. Perfectly manicured fingers weighted with sparkling diamonds picked at the delicacies in the ice-filled bowl, but usually when we finally rose from the table to continue the party elsewhere that evening, the seafood was belly up and floating in melted ice water.

After the restaurant lost its lease at the Sherry-Netherland Hotel, it was renovated into an inviting, light-filled restaurant named Cipriani's after its owner, Harry Cipriani, who was from an island off Venice, Italy, which also bore his name. Cipriani's was famous for a champagne-and-peach nectar drink called a "Bellini." Harry was credited for inventing this delicious drink that just about did us in one winter afternoon.

When Jan, Suzanne, Sandra, Julie, and I met for lunch, we arrived in our black limousines and all wore similar Blackglama mink coats. After hours of partying, and untold numbers of Bellinis, we struggled to stay focused just to find the hat-check girl and the front door. Fumbling with our tickets, we all simultaneously thrust them toward the confused young hat-check lady who hurriedly slipped the mink coats onto our shoulders. I was oblivious to the unfamiliar perfume that permeated my coat as we giggled our way out to our limos where they lined up in front of the restaurant. We each flopped into a limousine and sat stunned on the drive home.

One problem. In our confusion, there had been a fruit basket turnover of limos and black mink coats. I had Sandra's coat, hence the perfume, and everyone else was matched up with someone else's mink coat. That was a minor problem because we would all be reunited that night and could untangle the furry mixup then. The limo switch did, however, cause Jules a scare.

Never one to concern herself with the small details of life, like her address, Jules sank into the back seat of the limo and told the chauffeur to take her home. It turned out that it was

Suzanne's chauffeur, David, that she ordered home. The only problem with that was that he didn't know where her home was.

"David, you know where I live."

"Not really, Mrs. Boyce, I know the area."

"Oh, dear, well, just drive around and stop at the buildings, and we'll ask the doormen if they recognize me; the one that does, then that's the place I live."

52

GREG

THE DAY I RECEIVED THE NEWS THAT MY BROTHER, GREG, WAS going to marry his sweetheart, Alita, I spent several moments remembering all the other recent family weddings. To a close family such as ours, weddings were the highlights of our lives. They were opportunities for parents to demonstrate their pride in their family and to validate all the years of hard work, support, and love that brought them to this pivotal day. They were times to declare to the world, "There, we did it. We raised a handsome, responsible son, and now he will begin his own family."

I was honored to be Greg's best man and prepared myself to make my family proud that he had chosen me. Those were the years of deep tans, trim, well-toned bodies, and revoltingly small meals. It would be fair to say that I was obsessed with looking great and that I watched every morsel I ate.

During our annual European vacations, I would actually drop a few pounds because I couldn't weigh myself, and I feared I would gain an ounce. The thought of ballooning up and out of my provocative, sexy clothes made it easy to restrict my appetite. Oh, don't forget the drugs. They certainly helped replace hunger with mental and physical activity.

Anyway, when I arrived home for Greg's wedding, I looked like the star everyone treated me as.   With a quick wit and fabulous clothes, of course I was popular.   To my family, I was a living fairytale and a mystery.   (I'm sure that this book will clear up some of that.)

On the day of the wedding, Greg and I took a limousine to Notre Dame Church in North Caldwell, New Jersey.   I was feeling proud of my brother; he looked wonderfully handsome in his tuxedo on his special day.   For a few miles I did some reminiscing of our childhood together.   He was ten-and-a-half years younger than I was and had always lived in my shadow. So had my sister, Francesca, for that matter.

As the limo cruised toward the church, I really studied his kind face and saw not one bit of jealousy or resentment for having been dealt the hand of being my younger brother.   I'm sure I didn't realize just how painful it must have been for him hearing people constantly remark about my looks.   It seemed that I received all the favorable attention, and in most families, that can create an irrevocable break between siblings.   Greg's generous nature never held those memories against me.   After gushing over me, people would toss a grim smile toward my brother and sister and be on their way.   It was like Greg and Francesca were invisible.   Naturally, I adored the attention, but it deeply hurt me to see them frequently slighted.

We did a line of coke on the way to the church and Greg gave me a big smile and a few requests.   "Listen, Tony.   You know, this is my day.   Try to keep your ass out of the pictures as much as you can.   Try not to flaunt that pretty face of yours and let's just let me shine for once."   I laughed like hell because it was said with a great amount of humor and sincerity.

Out of the window I saw Notre Dame Church looming gloriously down the street.   Some guests and members of the wedding party were also arriving, and we slowed to join the line of vehicles waiting to be welcomed at the front door by the valet parking attendants.   I nudged Greg when I noticed my parents exiting their limousine up ahead.

God, Mom looked stunning.   She moved with such grace and elegance.   My father joined her on her right and offered her a familiar arm.   Together they ascended like angels into the church.

"There goes someone special, Greg.   You know, Mom and Dad have always been there for each of us and each other. How many other people can say the same?"

I daydreamed a bit.   "Remember when Mom would leave us a secret note in our lunch sack that said to come to the school office at twelve o'clock?   And then, she would spring us out of school for the rest of the afternoon and treat us to lunch and private time with her?   She did that for you also, didn't she, Greg?"

"Yes, God love her."

Just as I was about to get emotional, we exited the limo as Mom and Dad reached the top step and turned around.   Greg and I waved and bounded up the steps to embrace our wonderful parents.

Then we lost ourselves into the bowels of the church to laugh and while away the last minutes of Greg's freedom.   Soon we were greeted by their very good friend, Father Ben, the pastor of the church, and the Bishop of Newark.   I had not met the Bishop, and as I turned to shake his hand, he announced in front of Greg, "My, God, you must be Tony.   I've heard so much about you!"

Under his breath, Greg whispered to me, "Even the priest."

We bolted away and laughed like hell.   Greg whined, "I'm not in this church three seconds and I just give you this talk about not stealing the show from me and even the fucking priest has to come up and comment about you. Isn't that a bitch?"

We laughed about that throughout the entire wedding ceremony. Every time I got near him, he would whisper, "Even the fucking priest."

Other than that, the wedding was flawless. Alita was a heavenly vision in white. She seemed to float on a cloud of lace as she neared the altar. Several of us did notice, however, that Francesca was stoned and hysterically bawling her eyes out as she walked down the aisle. We found out later that, although she had never, ever taken any drugs or smoked a cigarette, she had taken a Quaalude given to her by her hairdresser to help calm her down. But even with a stoned sister and an over-shadowing brother, Greg had his perfect day.

53

Drowning Boy

While my friends, including the Spauldings and the Myles, experimented with tangled sexual escapades occupying many beds and many lovers, Brik and I wove a private cloak of fanciful and intense sexual drama.

But there was nothing I enjoyed more than hearing the latest sexual adventures from my friends. In Los Angeles we would meet at Trumps, across from Mortons, for high tea, and I would encourage them to tell all. For hours we would relive intimate details of passion and perversion as we sat so prim and perfectly groomed, an exquisite, classy entourage of decadence. From afar, onlookers probably thought our animated conversations were on the merits of a new art exhibit in town or the newest musical to open in Los Angeles.

Many of my married friends participated in the promiscuous practice of multiple sexual partners and wife swapping known as "swinging." With curious reservations, I watched the mating exchanges that captivated the lives of my associates during the 1970s and early 1980s. In retrospect, my reservations proved prophetic as one by one my friends' marriages fell into disarray.

At the sexual playground called Plato's Retreat, couples could enter a fanciful, borderless world of unlimited sexual pleasures. Sexual satisfaction was only limited by one's imagination, and, from the detailed accounts I received, a good time was had by all.

Brik and I didn't go to Plato's Retreat because in many ways it disgusted me. Besides, it was only for married, heterosexual couples. But exclusion from this famous playground didn't prevent us from immersing ourselves into our own private sea of erotica.

When closing the arched door of the North Bedford house, Brik left his straight, married life distantly behind him. I remember nights when he came through the front door with a soft glow in his eyes as he focused in on me advancing to greet him. This secret door of his life was the most satisfying in his garden of delights. The fame, wealth, adoration, and beautiful women were all his for the taking, but without our relationship he would have felt unfulfilled.

Ours was a relationship of deep love and commitment that burned for almost a quarter of a century, and, within the framework of our unity, we each thrived. His absences and other commitments afforded me opportunities to cultivate friendships, to travel and expand toward any horizon that attracted me. For my devotion and attentiveness, I was given the financial support that provided me with the luxuries of a privileged lifestyle.

To most outsiders, Brik's life was an open book of rehearsals, filming, openings, award shows, interviews, and marriage commitments, but when he escaped to his refuge, which was my world, he could really be himself. As he would back slowly into the closing door and follow my steps toward him, his entire demeanor changed. He would reach out to greet me with his dynamic smile and then relax into my arms. Our emotionally dependent relationship was strengthened by telephone calls throughout the day, whispered plans conveyed during dinners and outings, and spur-of-the-moment rendezvous we sometimes carved out of a busy day.

Unlike our friends, we didn't share our sexual love with others. Our theatric sexual encounters were private and only played for an audience of two. To heighten our sexual experiences, we used drugs like poppers known by the names Kryptonite, Bolt, and Rush, and other drugs like Quaaludes and Ecstasy. When using some of these drugs, our inhibitions would dissolve, and it was common to enjoy hours of intense lovemaking. The sense of touch seemed magnified a thousand fold, and something as ordinary as a light kiss on the back of the neck could create waves of pleasure far off the seismic scale.

To provide freshness to our sex life, we acted out elaborate scenarios where we called ourselves by different names and engaged in spontaneous dialogue. With the help of drugs, our play-acting took on such a reality that many times it actually felt as if we'd had sex with another person.

Sometimes in our dramas, I was scripted to be a waiter and Brik a customer. Other times I was an Olympic swimmer with Brik as my coach, or a boy cutting down a Christmas tree, or someone getting a massage from Mike the Masseuse. One evening I was a "drowning boy" and Brik played the heroic lifeguard who saved me from a watery death. This turned out to be one of Brik's favorites, and after I drowned over and over that evening and had been given enough "mouth-to-mouth" for the Titanic victims, I finally pleaded, "Just let me drown!"

After a night of life guarding, Brik would return the next morning to the "lights, cameras, and action!" and wave to his adoring fans clustered at the gates of the studio who were oblivious to his second and most heroic life guarding career.

54

CELEBRATIONS

MY DAILY CALENDAR WAS AS IMPORTANT TO ME AS MY TOOTHBRUSH; without it, my orderly world of parties, luncheons, dinners, trips, birthdays, and anniversaries would have broken apart like a 500-piece puzzle in a kindergarten classroom. When we weren't traveling or entertaining guests, we were partying.

Any occasion, from a birthday to the Charles and Diana wedding, was cause for celebration. Friends flew from coast to coast to surprise one another for annual birthday extravaganzas, and price was certainly not an object when it came to having a good, showy time. Take the all-white wedding of Sandra and Max Spaulding's daughter, Renee, for instance.

The grand ballroom at the Pierre Hotel was booked for this ultimate wedding that was shared with an intimate group of 325 of their closest friends and relatives. Every detail was carried out to perfection, including violin music and new paint for the ballroom and ladies' and men's rooms. The powder rooms had white trellises interwoven with greenery, and small soaps and hand towels had the bride and groom's initials on them.

At 2:00 a.m., after the formal affair successfully impressed the guests, the room was magically stripped of the white tablecloths. The $125,000 worth of white flowers disappeared and great yellow arrangements appeared in their place. Enough of the freakin' white, it was time to disco.

Oh, how did I know there were trellises in the ladies' room? I went in there and also into countless others from the east coast to the west coast and all over Europe, too. I frequently followed my lady friends into the powder rooms to laugh, gossip, and share a line of cocaine. Surprisingly, not once was I asked to leave a ladies' room, nor was there ever a shocked scream or even a cocked eyebrow of disapproval.

Another grand party that celebrated the 40th birthday of the vivacious Suzanne Worth was held in a sound studio in Manhattan. The theme was, naturally, the forties. The women wore veiled, pillbox hats, and the men came in dashing, 40s-style tuxedos. Entertainment was provided by the Manhattan Transfer, their catchy, cosmopolitan music perfectly complemented the electric-blue and black decorations.

Guests grabbed glasses of bubbling champagne and hors d'oeuvres from silver trays balanced on wooden, black cut-out waiters and waitresses stationed at the elevator entrance. Of course, real caterers glided through the crowd also. The party coordinators had taken care of every detail following the color and theme requests of the patrons. They were the ones responsible for the decorations, table clothes, napkins, and favors. In Suzanne's case, they even covered the entire room with electric-blue and black satin fabric.

After a few drinks, the room looked exactly like New York City at night, but without the muggers. Behind the band was a cut-out silhouette of the skyline of New York that was back lit by soft yellow lights. The puckered, black satin ceiling had twinkling star lights and even a crescent moon.

Suzanne's claim to fame was that she was a major shopper, so naturally her birthday cake was topped with a beautiful confectionery shopping bag. Her husband Daniel instructed her to reach into the shopping bag and get her birthday present, which was harder than it sounds.

The cake was six tiers high, and the shopping bag was built into the top layer. Suzanne's short, classy cut dark hair reflected starlight as she dragged a chair to the cake table. She hopped up on the chair, reached into the bag, and, to a hushed, attentive crowd, fished out and waved a three-inch-wide canary yellow and white antique diamond bracelet. Well, you only turn 40 once.

55

MARILYN

ONE OF THE HOTTEST, HIPPEST, AND—NOT TO MENTION—PINKEST
buildings on La Cienega Boulevard was the nightclub La Cage
aux Folles. Nestled among scores of restaurants and bars, La
Cage stood out with its pink paint job and striped awnings
grinning like welcoming teeth to passing traffic.

La Cage was where it was happening during the 1970s and
early 1980s. Female impersonators strutted their stuff on a
postage-stamp-sized stage covered with pink feathers while
crowds roared. I was constantly amazed at the talent and
creativity of the performers there. From our table, an arm's
length away from the stage, we were magically transported to a
Marilyn Monroe movie performance or Barbra Streisand's
Central Park concert. Some impersonators were awesome in
their legerdemain. Celebrities often entertained their guests
there or came to La Cage after their own performances and
could count on full-blown acts that rivaled the talent of the
people being imitated.

The star of the show was the emcee known as Gypsy, who
wielded his wit like a sharpened knife as he bantered with the

audience. Maybe it was the lights, but in a bony-shouldered way, and even with sparse hair scooped over the top of his head, he looked attractive (in a Mack the Knife sort of way). His cutting remarks could slit throats. Only fools waded in for a confrontation with Gypsy.

One of the best performers was Wayne. He ignited the imagination of the crowd with his dynamic impersonations. He and his brother Sonny loved show business, and Sonny could be gorgeous when he dressed up, but it was Wayne who was able to capture Marilyn Monroe's delicate, vulnerable personality to perfection and Cher's sexy vibrancy. Sonny's talents lay in the fashion end of performance; he cut a mean gown.

Before his transformation from a normal-looking guy to Marilyn Monroe, Wayne was an ordinary, forgettable face in the crowd, but once he donned the stiletto heels and zipped up the 22" back zipper of his pink chiffon cocktail dress, he was Marilyn. You could see it in his face; he became the same breathy caricature that Norma Jean created years ago.

With a dip, a swirl, and a coy, red-lipped smile, "Marilyn" would stride out into the streets of Los Angeles for a personality test-run. Her long, confident steps were somehow separate from her bobbing, bleached blond hair. People on the street would stop and stare when Marilyn passed their way and confusion ensued at the thought of seeing Marilyn Monroe in person.

"That was Marilyn wasn't it, Harry?"

"No, dear, remember she's been dead 23 years."

"Oh, of course, you're right dear."

56

COCAINE

"HELLO, MISS DOLLY?"

"Yeah, hi."

"This is Tony. I'd like to order a case of red wine, a case of chablis, and three cases of champagne for tonight."

"Okay, Doll. See you at 2:00, love."

That was how we ordered our drugs. No back alley drug deals for us.

We had met Miss Dolly at the La Cage aux Folles club. Miss Dolly and I struck up a conversation one evening and found we had two things in common: one was having a good time and the other was drugs.

Together we howled at the show and exchanged brief personal histories over a few glasses of champagne. She insisted on Cristal and I enjoyed Dom Perignon. After I learned of her occupation as cocaine entrepreneur, I figured that I could help support her thriving drug business. Miss Dolly was a heavyset lesbian with perfectly manicured nails and hair, and she always wore expensive black pantsuits with lots of gold jewelry that rattled and glittered as she zoomed around town on her little black motorcycle.

Her wonderful sense of humor and her dependability placed her high on my list of acquaintances. Ordering the drugs should have been a simple thing. After all, we had a code that associated a name of a wine to the kind of drug I wanted her to bring. And, yes, she delivered, usually in the dark of night.

The code revolved around the premise that we were ordering wine. "Red wine" meant Quaaludes, "white wine" meant cocaine, and "champagne" meant Ecstasy, or something like that. At 2:00 a.m., I never could get it straight anyway. We'd be so fucked up our order would just come tumbling out. "Miss Dolly, just bring us some of everything."

Shortly after ordering, the bell at the gate would announce the arrival of the little black Honda motorcycle. She would gun the engine and roar up to the front door with a black leather drawstring bag draped around her ample shoulders. "Come in, Miss Dolly! Come join us."

With a dramatic gesture, she would fluff her hair with those manicured nails, twirl the black bag, and then gently place it on the table where she released the drawstring to reveal a veritable pharmaceutical display of illegal drugs. Usually, we wanted cocaine and would pay her $100 a vial for the extremely pure stuff. The number of little brown bottles with black tops that she delivered were probably equal to the number of pizza deliveries in the area.

Not that we had to pay for all of it. Sometimes she would come for a sale, but after partying with us into the early morning hours, she would forget to charge us. Her sometimes lax business practices didn't ruin her career, however. It was the cops. I heard that she languished a while in jail, but after paying her debt to society, she began a new successful career as a photographer.

57

EFFIE'S

WHILE IN NEW YORK WE DINED AT THE FINEST RESTAURANTS. Quite quickly they got to know us well because many times we came as a group with a Hollywood star. At Morton's Restaurant, the waiters knew us so well they always asked us if we wanted regular portions or the smaller "coke" portions for those of us whose appetites had been dulled from cocaine.

Effie's, a famous Italian restaurant in Greenwich Village, was well known for its heavyset owner, Effie. All of the stars went there and part of the reason they enjoyed it so much was the entertainment of watching the owner's outrageous behavior. It was common to see celebrities like Andy Warhol, Rod Stewart, and Mia Farrow at Effie's. At any time of the day or night, there was a clamoring line of hopefuls just trying to get into the place.

Effie was a huge Jewish woman who relished keeping people waiting in line for hours. If she liked you, she'd seat you, but if she didn't, she would tell you to go fuck yourself. She would just tell customers, "Look, I'm never going to seat you. Get your asses out." It was obvious her manners and hygiene weren't great, but for some reason the place was hot and packed. For the privileged customers who actually got to eat there, it could be an uncommon dining experience.

Effie was all business in her mind and all boat in her body. In her tent dresses that draped on top of the most protruding fat folds of her hips, stomach, and thighs, she'd squeeze between tables to meet, greet, and insult customers. Once she told us, "Don't order any food here. You know you're not going to eat anything. Just order garlic rolls and get the fuck outta here."

Being at Effie's was similar to viewing a freak show. The curious patrons loved to watch the rejected customers get kicked out and the ambiance was a polar opposite from the regular, civilized, upscale haunts of the rich and famous. Her earthy, "devil may care" appearance belied her business sense, and that was intriguing to people.

My friend, Rex, once asked her, "Why don't you do coke and drop a few pounds?"

She replied, "I do."

Effie was fat and she flaunted it in the faces of the thin and wasted women who were still striving to lose "just ten more pounds." These women's eyes would gleam when comparing their bony wrists with her ham-sized arm ringed as it was with rolls of fat that lapped like waves over her tight fitting Rolex watch. (To counteract the opulence of the Rolex, she wore strands of pop beads around her neck.) I always had the feeling that they admired her loud, uncouth behavior, and in a small way lived vicariously through her. She had balls. Maybe that was part of the appeal of Effie's.

58

CRASH

ELISE DE ANGELO, A DUTCH BEAUTY WITH STRIKING BROWN EYES, was my constant companion during my Beverly Hills years. When we first met, her world of multiple homes in Lake Arrowhead and Beverly Hills, an apartment in Aspen, speed boats, and matching white Bentley cars was about to experience a fatal blow. Actually, it was her husband, Dean de Angelo, who was gunned down as a result of his involvement in shady business dealings. The love of her life, Dean, was buried in front of Marilyn Monroe's crypt in a small cemetery in Westwood. Elise thought he would have liked that.

Elise married well three times and had many affairs of the heart, but she always considered Dean her only true love. Throughout years of marriages, divorces, deaths, and affairs we remained closer than a brother and sister. Together we made a striking couple: blond Elise with a voluptuous, Gabor-like figure and Dutch accent, and her Italian friend—dark, intense, and handsome. If Brik and I weren't out as couples with the Spauldings or the Myles, Elise and I were out cocktailing at the Polo Lounge or the Four Seasons. We were always on the lookout for someone hot or rich for her to fall in love with and marry. I always figured everyone knew that I was gay and that Elise was single and looking. It didn't dawn on me until years later that guys thought we were a couple, which explained why no one ever came on to Elise. Another reason could have been her unapproachableness. She was so beautiful in spirit and body, she scared off the prime catches.

Brik's best friend, Clay Langford, a famous movie producer, became infatuated with Elise. Apparently his famous wife didn't know or care because Elise accompanied Clay as his mistress for years. Elise became a "beard" for Brik and me. A beard was a disguise. For example, Rock Hudson was always accompanied by a gorgeous woman to give him the appearance of being a ladies' man. When Brik, Clay, Elise, and I went out, the appearance was an acceptable, non-controversial combination of people. The curious simply couldn't tell who was with whom.

Elise and I shared intimate secrets, including personal details of our sex lives. Over several years, she confided that Clay began making some bizarre requests in the bedroom. Elise and I hovered over cocktails at the Four Seasons one evening and tried to figure Clay out. Lately, she disclosed, he had insisted on having bobby pins clamped to his nipples during sex. What was that? He later began wearing her undergarments, sexy negligees, and even her high heels. She confided that by the time he was ready for sex she didn't know whether to fuck him or send him to the Masquerade Ball. All of the drugs couldn't trick her mind enough to keep her from feeling that she was having sex with his ugly sister. Elise had no lesbian tendencies and in the end, it all became too mysterious and too much to take. Elise eventually left Clay, but not before our near death experience in Puerto Rico.

Once, the four of us flew to Puerto Rico for a private beach vacation at the renovated Rockefeller estate known as the Dorado Beach Hotel, where everyone had individual bungalows with walkways to the sparkling blue water. Dorado Beach Hotel was about 45 minutes from San Juan and was known for its casino and fabulous golf course that hugged the ocean shoreline. We had everything at our disposal, including room service that brought us delicious meals, beautifully served on our private terraces overlooking the beach.

One idyllic morning as we languished under a yellow beach umbrella with our friends, Brik presented his plan for fun. Elise and I were very content with our cold drinks and summer paperback books, our butts settled firmly into concave dents in the sand. I had been secretly checking out Clay's nipples from behind my shades to confirm Elise's shocking bedroom confessions. (I couldn't tell.)

Brik announced that we were all going to fly to St. Thomas for a day. To some that may sound romantic, but to me it sounded like a great way to ruin a fabulous vacation. Who wanted to fly Island Wings, those little, glued-together gnats called airplanes? Everyone but me, it turned out.

"If that's what you want to do, fine; go, but I'm staying here in paradise," I declared.

"Oh, Tony, it won't be fun without you. Nothing's going to happen, come on."

My protestations didn't end there, but in the end I agreed to go. Why were we going to fly the 45 minutes to St. Thomas? To shop. But I didn't need anything. Didn't need jewelry or perfume, I didn't need anything, at least not then. Later, I almost needed a cemetery plot.

Elise and Clay took an earlier flight. By the time I was goaded onto another plane by Brik's verbal prodding,

"Pansy...Faggot," I was a nervous wreck. From the moment the tilted, bouncing plane rolled out from behind a cement block building, I knew I wasn't drunk enough or high enough.

The breeze from the sputtering propeller barely bent over the weeds growing up in the dirt runway. "No way," I thought. It taxied to a stop in front of Brik, a honeymooning couple, and me. I was lagging back, protecting myself from the awful truth, that we were about to board a Wright brother's reject. The engine was killed, and the propeller instantly stopped as if it were thinking, "Thank God. Made it this far."

The young couple climbed aboard; the guy strategically caressed her butt as he guided his new bride into the back of the flying casket. Brik leaped up next, and I advanced with shaky legs. I grabbed onto the scratched aluminum door frame and pulled myself up, expecting to sit next to Brik but was quick to realize that my seat was going to be in the cockpit in the copilot's place. Oh, shit.

My fingers fumbled with the beat-up safety harness until I heard a click. I turned around and clubbed Brik on the knee with my fist and heard him snicker. The pilot had walked into the cement building for some last-minute provision, like a rosary perhaps. He spit and checked his zipper as he shuffled across the hot dirt. Why, oh why, couldn't he have looked like John Glenn or even Howard Hughes?

Flinch was his nickname. I didn't ask. He wore a red faded baseball hat that announced "Boobs, Inc." across the top. I didn't ask about that, either. He proudly announced that he had been lured back from retirement and was damn glad to be back in the saddle again. His old, swollen fingers unwrapped a stick of Black Jack gum and tossed the powdery wrapper out the window. He held up the pack and offered his passengers a modest refreshment. We all declined.

Flinch grabbed a pair of sunglasses off the instrument panel and turned the key. With a big smile, he turned and saluted us, showing a huge safety pin that held his glasses together. He hadn't closed the fragile door yet because he wanted to check for incoming traffic and to spit one last time. I hit Brik again. A papery thud announced that his door was closed; another nail in the coffin, I thought.

Flinch's unwavering confidence and light-hearted comments did nothing to reassure me. I sat triggered for trouble. The few dials on the instrument panel spun, crept, and balanced about and meant absolutely nothing to me, but I watched them intently. I was, after all, the copilot. We flew at a low altitude that was like good news, bad news.

The good news was, of course, not as far to fall. The bad news was it was possible to study every rise and fall of the turbulent waves below. That negated the good news. I should have made it into the *Guinness Book of Records* for the most number of "Hail Marys" said in a 45-minute period.

Before we reached St. Thomas, the winds gusted up and began tossing us around like a frisbee. I tried to smack Brik again, but I missed during a violent downdraft. The little airport at St. Thomas looked like a moving target. Even the instrument needles were confused, not that the pilot noticed. He was loving it.

"YEE-ha," he yelled my way as he wrestled with the throttle.

Hell, what did he care if we died? He was almost dead anyway.

"Oh, Jesus!" I heard myself yell as the stormy winds grabbed at us like a helpless bird in a hurricane.

Something really bad happened, I guess, because Flinch grabbed the hand-held microphone and yelled, "May day, May day. We're going down!" I grabbed Flinch around the neck and tried to kill him before he could do it to us.

"Dear, Jesus! Help us," I screamed. I stopped my assault on Flinch when I realized I wouldn't want to meet my maker with a homicide on my record.

Gusts of wind knocked us around and off the runway. The right wing grabbed some shrubs, and we were spun around to an undignified stop. Before help arrived, I looked around weakly. Old Flinch was knocked out, Brik was groaning with broken ribs, and even though I couldn't see the newlyweds through the blood trickling down my face, I could hear them reciting the Lord's Prayer in the back seat.

We struggled to grasp the reality that we had survived. Somehow I managed to turn and lash out at a crumpled-over Brik, shouting, "You fucking asshole. I didn't want to come here anyway!"

I railed on awhile until the groom started screaming, "Get out! Get out! It's going to blow up."

That was all I needed to hear. The stunned group struggled to get free of the safety belts; sirens wailed; and lights of the arriving rescue vehicles flashed while we escaped the wreckage.

From the gurney in the emergency room, I glared at Brik who was strapped down next to me. "Pick a plot," I said.

"What?" he coughed.

"Pick a fucking plot. I ain't leaving this place."

For five days I refused to leave. Finally, they slipped a "mickey" in my drink, and when I awoke, I was back at the Dorado Hotel. Thank you, God.

59

Oscars

After going to several of the Oscar ceremonies, we became somewhat jaded. It wasn't that we were given bad seats; we always got strategically located seats. It wasn't that it wasn't interesting to see the gowns and jewels and be part of the worldwide curiosity. Frankly, it wasn't a lot of things, including fun.

First, we had to be dressed and in our limousines well before 5:00 p.m. because we had to be seated before the event started at 6:00 p.m. Our poor driver would queue up in a mile-long line of limos and ease us up to the red carpet, where we would smile and jostle our way into the theater. People in the rowdy crowd would strain to be the first to locate an arriving star.

As my date and I walked by, someone yelled, "Hey, who's that?"

"Oh, he's nobody," replied another. (If they only knew.)

Brik would follow with our friends and finally be spotted with screams, "There's Brik Moor!"

Once inside, we were seated and resigned ourselves to being locked in our chairs for the next three hours. Oh, of course, it was possible to get up to go to the bathroom, but that was no simple act at the Oscars. There were men and women dressed up to blend into the crowd; these "runners" would practically leap into vacant seats in order for the panning cameras to avoid televising an empty space.

Prior to the big night, Oscar guests were mailed protocol instructions for the evening—"Don't do drugs while the camera is on you. Don't be taking a hit of cocaine. Don't say things like 'fuck you' if you lose." Surprisingly enough, people in the audience would bend over and do a line of coke or take a nip of something throughout the ceremony. All of that went on when the camera was pointed in the other direction.

At the last Oscars we attended, Bette Midler was a presenter who lit up the stage with her radiant smile and her multicolored gown. She said laughingly to the audience, "I didn't know what color to wear tonight, so I just wore them all." We were an arm's length away from movie stars like Jack Nicholson, Diane Keaton, Warren Beatty, and Lorenzo Lamas. Everyone had side comments to everything.

The outrageous comments really made the three-hour incarceration bearable. Of course, drugs loosened the tongues of the wittiest and cruelest, too. As Bette Midler was introduced, someone behind me said, "Who's she?"

"Who's she!" yelled a Hollywood legend, standing up to defend the Divine Miss M; "Who are you? The only thing you ever did was to fuck that duck in that sci-fi disaster." That brought down the whole house, and they quickly cut away for a commercial.

After that, Oscar night was at the Spaulding's suite in the Beverly Hills Hotel located on Sunset Boulevard. The magnificent pink hotel was a magnet for the rich and famous: luxurious suites and bungalows decorated with white-and-black marble and beautiful fabrics. Private gardens and patios provided elegant surroundings for any type of mischief. All the stars hung out here, and at its famous bar, The Polo Lounge, it was possible to catch a glimpse of the most famous celebrities in the world.

When the "New York contingent" flew in to party, they stayed at the Beverly Hills Hotel. This is also where I had a cabana at the pool. My house didn't have a pool, so I had a cabana at the Beverly Hills Hotel for entertaining guests. It was a lovely place for luncheons, and the convenient location was minutes away from the heart of Beverly Hills.

At the Beverly Hills Hotel we began an annual celebration of the Oscars with a special twist. We would order room service and turn on the Oscars on the television and give out our own awards, like "Who was the biggest pig of the group." The funniest award I remember was the Hershael Bernardi Sympathy Award given by Robert Myles to his wife Jan. He rose from his chair, tapped on his glass with a silver spoon and said, "And now to give the Hershael Bernardi Sympathy Award is last year's recipient, Kate Smith." We almost died.

Jan returned fire. Clink, clink, "And now, esteemed guests, we have a new award for a movie-in-progress starring Jack Klugman as Robert Myles." We had much more fun giving our own awards than we ever did at the real Oscars.

60

GRACE

In the summer of 1980, Brik and I were with friends on our annual trek to the South of France when we found out we were going to be received at the Palace of Monaco and would get to meet Princess Grace and Prince Rainier III. I can't remember how it happened, but Sandra and Max Spaulding were good friends with the Prince and Princess and wanted to introduce us to them.

Up until that night I had never been nervous about meeting anyone in my life. Nor was there ever any kind of apprehension about what they thought of me because I didn't care. But when it came to meeting royalty, that was a whole different thing.

That evening we were at the Hotel de Paris in Monte Carlo preparing for cocktails with the Prince and Princess. In my stocking feet, I crossed the elegant, antique-filled room, threw open the double French doors to our balcony overlooking the sea, and examined our destination that evening, the Prince's Palace. The sky was saturated with colors that hung in the air as the sun slowly set on paradise. Strategically located on the rocky hill above the Mediterranean Sea, the pink Palace evoked its Moorish heritage with great fortress walls and rounded sides. For centuries it had symbolized the presence of the Principality of the Grimaldis, and that night I was going to meet Monaco's Serene Highnesses.

From the balcony, I turned and watched Brik dress for the occasion. With an easy confidence, he pulled on his jacket and looked around for me. I shivered, not from a chill, but from nervousness. I padded back into our luxurious room and stood before the full-length dressing mirror. The white Versace shirt with its french cuffs was the perfect complement to the dark gray Armani suit I had chosen to wear that evening. I watched myself button the shirt and slip the 24-carat gold, Tiffany cuff links into place. With a slight tug, I lined them up. In the reflection I could see Brik relaxing with a drink. Again and again, I combed my hair and checked for specks of dust on my flawless jacket. It felt like I was going to my first prom.

Our friends arrived and gave us last minute instructions about the proper protocol for meeting a prince and princess. Sandra said, "Okay, you bow to the Prince and I curtsy to the Princess, and then you bow to her and curtsy to him," or something like that.

Over and over, I practiced the routine, but there was a mental block I couldn't conquer. I was so confused, I asked, "Can't I just say, 'Hi, it's nice to meet you'?"

Brik smiled, "Gosh, Tony, I've never seen you like this before. What are you so nervous about?"

"What do you mean?"

"Get a hold of yourself, you know Grace Kelly's father was in construction. She did exactly what you did; she married well."

After I picked myself up off the floor and thought about it, I had to agree that he was right. She came from Philadelphia, her father was in construction. So was my family. Sure, she was a movie star. I was used to them. She had won an Oscar. So what? She was beautiful. Yeah. Okay, she married a prince. That was her big thing. She had done the same thing I had done, married well.

Brik's insight relieved my mind, and I forgot my uneasiness. I don't know if the lines of coke we did before leaving helped, too, but by the time the Palace limousine was sent for us, I was the old, confident Tony again.

It was early evening when we were driven through the walled entrance to the Palace. Beautiful lighting illuminated the cascading potted plants and window boxes. There was a magnificent fountain surrounded by a curved, Belgian block drive leading up to the stark, pink palace. I was intrigued by the number of servants—footmen, doormen, a protocol person, maids, and gardeners who dotted the estate.

We were invited into a grand receiving room filled with family and political overtones. Huge, individually lit portraits glared down on visitors from ornate gilded frames. Looming overhead were oversized colorful flags that saluted the ancestors and declared the political and historical importance of the Royal Family. Abundant fresh flower arrangements brought beauty, color, texture, and heavenly aromas to the Palace of Monaco. Besides meeting Princess Grace, the exquisite flower arrangements were my favorite memory of that night.

We were greeted by a protocol expert who went through the bowing, curtsying routine. Then we were escorted to a smaller receiving room furnished with two sofas, divided by a table between them, and a rich, pale green-and-gold-leaf tapestry wallpaper. Out of the corner of my eye, I caught a glimpse of the realistic fresco of clouds painted on the ceiling. Prince Rainier was standing with a drink in his hand.

When he saw us, he put his drink down and advanced toward us. The Prince was so at ease, he kissed Sandra, hugged Max, and reached out to shake our hands after we bowed slightly. Funny, I thought, he didn't act like a prince, or really even look like one. I had envisioned being greeted by someone wearing a dark tailored suit with a satin sash crusted with medals, embroidery, and a four-foot sword stuck in a shiny, black leather sheath. Prince Rainier was elegant, however, in his handsome, dark blue suit. There was one mysterious thing about his appearance, one concession to position—on his jacket was a bar-shaped pin with colorful stripes. Maybe this was a modest way of declaring his authority.

I must admit my heart skipped a beat when Princess Grace entered the room. Wearing a pink Chanel suit, she floated across the room, and I was transported to the realm of the angels. Under the frescoed clouds and to imaginary trumpets, Grace majestically walked up to me and smiled.

It was a magical hour of light conversation, champagne, and caviar on toast, enough time to study a universal icon of class. Princess Grace wore a pink hair band to match her dress, a diamond pin, a simple gold wedding band, and a blue sapphire-and-diamond pinky ring. It was heartwarming to watch Grace's and Rainier's soft smiles to one another. During conversations, I caught their intimate glances and quickly saw that they were a very loving and caring couple.

The hour ended too quickly, but this proved to be only the first of many spent with Her Serene Royal Highness, or however that went. To me she was Grace and I'm proud to have called her friend. Over the next one-and-a-half years, we partied and laughed together on many occasions.

A beautiful box from Grace arrived at Christmas in 1981. In it was a complete place setting for 12 of Limoges turn-of-the-century china from the Hotel de Paris. Months later, there was further correspondence from the Palace of Monaco. Sadly, it was Grace's funeral invitation.

61

DAVIS

MANY TOOK TO HEART THE FAMOUS SAYING, "FASTEN YOUR seatbelts, it's going to be a bumpy night," when Bette Davis was around. This legendary, self-assured woman commanded those in her presence with a voice like that of a defiant victim of a two-handed chokehold around her papery neck. Her brief words erupted from her red lipstick-smeared mouth with a flat, staccato rhythm. Not surprisingly, people tended to do whatever she required of them. First, there was the Hollywood Star factor; second, there was the fear she would put a spell on them with her bulging eyes, that she might become enraged and fitful, maybe even temporarily reincarnate Hush, Hush, Sweet Charlotte.

We were at an Oscar party one evening at Wolfgang Puck's restaurant, Spago's, on Sunset Boulevard. Electricity was in the air as actors, producers, directors, and their entourages arrived in limousines, some waving a golden Oscar, some waving a cigar. Sparkling diamond jewelry reflected the flashbulbs of the crowded paparazzi clustered at the front door. One-of-a-kind designer dresses clung to barely hidden breasts, and there were the welcomed occasional fashion mistakes that created shocked looks and a place on Mr. Blackwell's list.

As he had done for many years, Swifty Lazar hosted the flashiest Oscar party at Spago's. We were invited as guests of Irving Rapper, the director for Now Voyager, a good friend of Mae West's, and a very dear friend of ours.

Bette Davis was across the room, a ghostly apparition in a cloud of layered smoke, a wrinkled hand grenade surrounded by fascinated well-wishers who longed to meet her so that they could brag about it later to someone who might care.

I was across the room with a good buzz on, entertaining friends with nonstop stories, when Irving came over and said that Bette Davis wanted to meet me.

I said, "Bette Davis would like to meet me? Get out." After some time, however, I wandered over toward Bette.

She zeroed in on me, commanding, "Come here."

I did.

"You're quite an entertaining boy."

"Thank you, Miss Davis."

"You are to come to my house for cocktails, Tuesday at 7:00 p.m. Get my number. Call my houseman, and let us know."

Of course, we went. No one could, or would, say "No" to Bette Davis.

She lived in an apartment in West Hollywood. That Tuesday evening we walked up to her apartment and were almost overwhelmed by the cigarette smoke practically billowing out from under the front door. We rang the doorbell and were greeted by a Portuguese maid in scuffies who couldn't have cared less. (Flash-a Baby Jane Christmas gift?)

She bellowed, "Miss Davis, your company has arrived."

Brik and I stumbled into the cave-like apartment and were led to a dark room with a round, wooden coffee table around which five or six people perched on small, stool-like chairs. The glow of Bette Davis' cigarette guided us to our stools, where we were quickly offered a cocktail.

There we sat, drinks in hand, circled around the table. As my eyes adjusted to the darkness of the heavily draped room, I thought that I would spot some hors d'oeuvres on the table, but all that appeared was a wooden bowl of pretzels, some peanuts, and stale Bugles. Not a piece of sterling in sight.

It was common for the older movie stars to have light-defying drapes in their homes. In the old movie days, lighting was not sophisticated and was always very hot and glaring. When they came home from the studio and partying, the stars required a dark house for quiet, restful seclusion. Some friends of ours, Bob and Paul, bought Susan Hayward's apartment in Ft. Lauderdale in the Four Seasons and said it also had heavy drapes that reeked with the stench of years of cigarette smoke and where after a emotional fit Susan heaved her Oscar into Sunset Lake off the Intra-coastal waterway which was later dredged for its recovery.

I was barely over the disappointment of having "no food" when I really noticed the stool-like chairs on which we were sitting. Each was different in style, yet similar in size and was topped with a cushion covered with a fine needlepoint design.

Bette's only real conversation that evening was to announce, "Now, we're on the same level." That brought a wicked smile to her face as we were informed that we were sitting on antique wooden toilets she had gathered from all over the world. Everyone shifted around a bit at the uncomfortable thought of their stool's nasty history.

Bette theatrically lifted her cigarette holder and demanded, "Light my butt!"

The maid shuffled over with a lighter and a look that could kill, and lit the cigarette. You could see that Davis wanted to kick the shit out of her like in Baby Jane.

Other than that, Bette never said a word, never contributed anything to the conversation. The rest of the guests told some stories and after about half an hour, Bette rose from her toilet-chair, crept half-way across the room, turned toward us, dramatically raised her cigarette holder to her shriveled lips, puffed, and announced, "It's...OVER!" With that she left the room. (Not such a bumpy night after all.)

We all stared at one another. She had left the room; therefore, it must be over. We were dismissed like prisoners by a prison matron and silently filed out. I sent a thank-you note and flowers, but I never heard from her again. Maybe she had been entertained for a few minutes, or maybe she hated us. Who knows? We were, however, given a fabulous exiting line that we used on more than one occasion. Any time I wanted to leave a party or an event, I would whisper in Brik's ear, "It's OVER!"

62

ROLLS

THE BEDFORD HOUSE WAS A LOVELY PLACE TO LIVE, BUT IT WAS rather modest by Beverly Hills' standards. Because Brik was enjoying phenomenal success in his movie and television careers, he began to feel that the Bedford place was not pretentious enough to reflect his star status. Of course, it wasn't his house. I lived there, managed it, cared for it, and was responsible for its upkeep while he lived with his wife, Wallace, some distance away.

These were the prime years of Brik's stardom and he was receiving a lot media attention. He became the focus of trailing paparazzi anytime he was out in public. Magazine photographers were obsessed with his beautiful wife and her modeling career, as well as their glamorous, jet-setting lifestyle. He and Wallace made a handsome couple and were endlessly photographed almost to the point of becoming the 1970s symbol of star royalty. Their smiles appeared on every tabloid in grocery store checkout lines across the country during the late 1970s and early 1980s. They seemed to be showing that, yes, it was possible to have it all...beauty, notoriety, wealth, and a stunning mate.

As little old ladies unloaded their shopping carts, I'm sure they paused momentarily, adjusted their bifocals, skimmed the bold headlines, and fantasized at the images depicted on the covers of the magazine. The fixings for their evening meal moving along the conveyor belt toward the cashier, they must have felt somehow cheated by the unfairness of life. How could they know that the tabloid's happy embrace captured by the photographer at the airport terminal was taken as Brik and Wallace prepared to take separate flights, she to a New York opening, and Brik to the South of France to be with me on the beautiful Mediterranean Sea? Okay, I'll take a trip to France or New York over an evening of pot roast, but, unlike the grocery bill of a few bucks, my price became much greater.

When I was informed that we would look for a larger, more prestigious house my intuition kicked in and I cringed. I must admit I did feel a bit excited about moving and having the challenges of redecorating and furnishing a new place, but I could sense trouble brewing. After all, I knew that Hattie and I simply couldn't manage a larger house without hiring additional help and that meant trouble.

Before I got involved in the process of locating another home, however, Brik found and gave to me a beautiful colonial house on North Beverly Drive. The 15-room North Beverly Drive house had plenty of amenities: separate maid's quarters, a huge master bedroom suite, and terraced gardens in the back with a gazebo, but its best feature was the privacy it afforded me. I quickly launched into decorating the house, and for months I was busy with all of the decisions and planning necessary to get the enormous job completed. The house, with its luscious, hunter green carpet and hardwood floors, was an exquisite final house for me in Los Angeles.

A 100-year-old magnolia tree graced the front lawn and it was one of the first things a visitor saw after entering through the brick-and-iron front gates of the estate. The house was half brick, then white with hunter green shutters. The dining room was decorated in black and pink moiré, with balloon curtains and touches of greens. It was gorgeous.

The great room had a beige-and-apricot theme. The master bedroom was grayish blue with black lacquer furniture, and the guest bedroom, with its attached sitting room, was a study in Laura Ashley. The canopy bed was the centerpiece. I chose greens, whites, and a little pink for these rooms. The house was so tastefully done, it was photographed for the Beverly Hills magazine *213*.

Very shortly after moving in, I walked out to get the mail, even though that was the staff's job. As I walked down to the mailbox, a bouncing, blond, big-titted Barbie came running out of the house from across the street. It must have been a painful journey without the high heels she apparently was used to wearing because she ran over barefoot on her tiptoes yelling frantically, "Excuse me. Excuse me. We've been seeing all these stars and limos coming to your house, and we's all wondering who you are?"

Not a "Good morning" or "My name is blah-blah," just "we's all wondering who you are?"

I looked at her and asked, "Well, excuse me, who are you?"

"Oh, I'm the lady of that house." She pointed her manicured nails.

I thought that I would just wreck her. "Well, I'm the lady of that house." I turned and walked back through the gate.

One morning shortly after I moved in, a package arrived. It was from Brik, who was always generous and thoughtful. Once, while shopping in Paris, I'd become entranced with a crystal Lalique swan that appeared to be floating on a mirrored lake, complete with ripples.

"Oh, that's beautiful. Wouldn't it be exquisite as a dining room centerpiece?" It was just a simple, wishful statement for something so elegantly beautiful, in a city saturated with the finest of the fine. I had merely seen it in a store and Brik had apparently remembered my awed appreciation and had had it sent to me for a housewarming gift. For years it was the focal piece of my dining room table. Tiny pin lights illuminated the rippled mirror with the crystal swan and fresh rose petals sprinkled around the decoration to make a breathtaking, simple centerpiece.

Several days after the Lalique swan arrived, another housewarming gift from Brik was delivered to the North Beverly Drive house. I answered the door and saw two cars in the driveway. A young guy handed me a set of keys and hopped into the first car and sped away. The remaining vehicle was a two-toned, blue Rolls-Royce complete with real platinum pinstriping—a magnificent Silver Shadow II with a navy blue interior.

In Los Angeles, the most prestigious people's vehicles are parked near the entrances of restaurants or other establishments for a quick getaway. I never had to ask for this car to be out front. It was such a beautiful car, it was always parked near the front door where many people admired it and were impressed by its classy beauty. I must admit that there is nothing like driving a Rolls, but there's nothing like replacing a missing hubcap for $1,200 either!

North Beverly Drive became the backdrop for the drama of the last years I spent in Los Angeles. Perhaps what the people scanning the tabloid headlines don't realize is that with all the luxuries comes a hell of a lot of grief. In every aspect of my life I had more than I'd ever had in my life: more houses, more cars, and more responsibilities. I could faintly hear the violin finale playing in the distance.

In the smaller houses I had owned, it had just been Hattie and me. Now, my drama had a new cast of characters that included Consuela, Sammy, and Suei. The new house staff complicated my life in numerous ways, and, even though I needed them, I despised the confusion and intrusion they caused.

First, it hurt my feelings that they secretly called me "Mommy Dearest." Unknown to them, I could hear their conversations in the servants' quarters. My suite was over the servants' area and their conversations drifted up to my attentive ears. And even though I fixed a delicious midday meal for them every Friday and gave them a two-hour break to enjoy it, they were like snakes.

I figured that having four house staff entitled me to a clean house, but they didn't see it that way. Upon arriving for the day, they would gather and begin their cutting comments and lazy bellyaching.

"How's the woman of the house? I hope he isn't too hung over."

"How's Mommy Dearest today?"

"I do hope he doesn't want us to clean the chandeliers."

Even if I did have a hangover and felt horrible, I would collect every sparkling, perky bone in my body, sash my Sanchez robe, and march downstairs humming a sadistic tune.

"Goooooood morning everyone. I hope everyone is feeling great this fine morning because today is 'chandelier day.'" I acted totally unaware of the horrified glances bouncing from Consuela, Sammy, and Suei as I made my way to the kitchen.

Having a house staff was a necessary curse. The North Beverly house required more care than Hattie and I could give it alone. But living my life in front of backstabbing employees wasn't my idea of living at all. Because they could blackmail us at anytime—go to the tabloids, talk shows, or newspapers, we were inclined to make peace with them at any cost. They knew that we knew they had us by the balls.

Consuela kept the house and did some cooking and turned out to be the biggest thief in the world. Robin Hood should have had her on his team. A black gay guy, Sammy, was a major-domo who took great advantage of us. He did the heavy work; and Hattie, who was up in years, did the laundry. Every Tuesday and Friday, Suei came and prepared beautiful, fresh flower arrangements. Also on Fridays, two guys came to clean and wax the Mercedes and Rolls, and later the limousine.

When I was away, Sammy had my cars at his disposal and even told people that it was his house and that I was his servant. As nasty as Sammy was, however, nothing prepared me for the betrayal I felt from Consuela.

Behind her back, Hattie accurately called Consuela, "Cuntswela." Her other nickname was "Elephant-ass." Consuela never made it a straight shot anywhere. She waddled from side to side. I swear that she logged more miles going sideways than she ever did moving forward. And from behind, Hattie had it right, "Tony, that elephant-assed, cake-making bitch better look out." Her ass had probably started out looking normal in her youth, but the years of languishing at her "master's" kitchen table had smashed her ass flat as two clay balls run over by a dump truck.

And she always had a rag. There were always tears. "Oh, Sir," sniffle, sniffle, "My granddaughter, Renita, is so heavy. The other children won't play with her. We can't find clothes to fit."

"What is it that you want, Consuela?"

"I see a new fat-free diet that might help, but it is very expensive for me who makes so little." Stab, stab.

"How much, Consuela?"

"Oh, thank you sir!"

Another time it was a long-suffering nephew, just out of prison, who wanted a chance to start over with a car repair business. There went another ten grand down the drain. I was a hopelessly easy touch, and they knew it.

We purchased our food from the Premier Market in Beverly Hills. The Premier Market could provide the finest, most comprehensive array of delectables to its customers, but, of course, its services came with a hefty price.

I remember ordering some asparagus and three kinds of ground meats for a meatloaf. I had placed the call and was cheerfully assured that it would be promptly delivered, which it was. The one pound of asparagus was tied with a thin bow and cost $12. The one pound of chuck, pork, and veal was patted into smooth mounds and wrapped in crackling white paper. Cost? $70. Then there was the liquor. There was a place on Robertson Drive called Robert Burns' Liquors. I would call and order cases of wine and cases of champagne, and I never really knew the cost of things. It was just delivered.

Liquor, candles, food, and linens were stockpiled in huge amounts to ensure that I was prepared for any entertaining emergency. It was years later, when I finally had the guts to fire her, that I discovered Consuela's generous side. I was so uninformed about the cost of things, I didn't realize that the huge food and liquor bills coming to the house had a direct correlation to the Consuela-prepared feasts she was making and taking to her friends who worked at Premier! She would order and cook pot roasts and hams and go bouncing down to the Premier Market to feed half the world. I could only imagine the quantity of stuff she took from the house for her own family.

Once as I prepared to leave for my six-week summer vacation, I told her to take the food from the refrigerator to her family. When I arrived back from the holidays everything was wiped out from the refrigerator, freezer, and even the spices in the pantry. I was furious, "Consuela, I said take the perishable food. You've taken everything!"

"Oh, Sir, you said to take food. I was only following your wishes."

Right.

63

BLUE CHEESE

OUR LIFE IN THE 1980s WAS ONE OF EXTREME EXCESS. IF A NUN'S life is a black-and-white pen sketch that reduces the necessities of life to the basics, ours was one of colorful, neon overkill. We did everything with exaggerated flair. We ate and dressed too well, traveled extravagantly, bought and sold homes and cars at a whim, acquired the best of everything imaginable (then didn't have time to enjoy it), and pumped up the volume by doing drugs and drinking alcohol, lots of alcohol.

And Brik and I weren't alone. Our married friends were experimenting with all of the above, plus several of the couples began a downward marital spiral by bringing others into their beds. One couple employed a stunningly handsome chauffeur who was good at more than driving, and their pretty young maid was easily persuaded to join them under the Egyptian, 300-thread-count, custom-made cotton sheets.

At first, they enjoyed three-way sex, and then, just as I had suspected, each partner swam solo into the oceans of pleasure. This was the beginning of the end for several of my friends' marriages, and I helplessly watched the disintegration that was a direct result of an overly indulgent lifestyle.

Brik and I indulged, too. We enjoyed cocaine for years; then we stopped that wonderful foolishness, and just drank liquor. As my blessed grandmother said, I was charmed from the start, because I dared death on many occasions and taunted trouble on a daily basis, but somehow escaped major disasters.

One of the perks of being known in Beverly Hills was that the cops really protected us and came to our rescue on more than one drunken occasion. It was like a close-knit family; they would protect us from our own follies. Sometimes they would slap a ticket on us and then drive us home when we'd been drinking too much.

Once I did a U-turn on Wilshire Boulevard, and a cop pulled me over.

"Tony," he said, "how much were we drinking this evening?"

I said, "Well, how bad was it?"

"You just did a U-turn in the middle of Wilshire Boulevard."

"Oh."

"Tell you what, Tony, just move over, and we'll get you home."

And they did.

On another night, Brik and I drove up the coast to Malibu to have dinner at the Chart House, a wonderful place to enjoy seafood, steaks, and the sunset. We had a magnificent view from our table nestled beside a picture window overlooking the ocean. The Chart House was built on stilts and catapulted its customers out over the lapping waves of the Pacific Ocean (an ocean we would become intimately familiar with before the evening's end). We had drinks before we left home and then ordered more at dinner. I anxiously grabbed a plate at the salad bar and heaped on the fresh, beautifully displayed delights. When there was room for nothing else, I smothered it all with blue cheese dressing and extra crumbles of blue cheese that clumped onto the top like dirty snowballs to Mt. Everest. On my way back to the table, I stumbled down some stairs and fell onto the salad plate. At that point, not only was I stinking from the booze, I reeked of blue cheese. A kindly waiter found another shirt for me, but my pants and shoes could have warded off evil with the deadly smell of decaying cheese. Not that this necessarily bothered us; we were too shitfaced to notice.

After a brief argument over whether Brik or I should drive home, Brik dropped into the driver's seat of his blue convertible Mercedes, and I closed the door on the passenger side reluctantly. The miles flew by as we careened down the Pacific Coast Highway. The ocean did a slow dance under the bright moon spotlight. Not that I noticed. I was counting my last earthly moments as tires screeched and the car listed from side to side depending on which curve we were speeding through. Great chuckles were erupting from Brik as he manhandled the steering wheel with great flourishing spins.

Finally, the road curved, but we didn't. The beautiful Mercedes tracked straight off the road, across the sand, and into the ocean. Thank Heavens we had the top down. Great swells of seawater poured into the car and slimy seaweed washed over the dark leather seats as we clamored out, laughing our asses off. Thankfully, there were no paparazzi around because they would have had a field day with that.

The police arrived and all I remember them saying is "Whew! Damn! What have you boys been drinking and eating?"

Without another unkindly word, they loaded us up and drove us home. The next day Brik had a wrecker pull the ruined car out of the deep, and promptly bought a new Testarossa. No problem, he'd been wanting one for a while anyway.

64

LUCY

I KNEW LUCILLE BALL, TOO, BUT I WISH I HADN'T KNOWN HER AT that period of my life. Somewhere encapsulated into the mind of every American who lived during the 1950s, 1960s, and early 1970s are remarkably clear images of Lucille Ball. There is the frantic candy assembly line scene; the tottering, long trailer full of rocks; her gorgeous, heavily lashed, wide-open eyes that seemed to gravitate her toward trouble—her haplessness, innocence, and beauty revive wonderful memories in most Americans.

It was through Lucy that women everywhere could live vicariously on the edge; have narrow escapes, observe family fights and turmoil, and then, 28 minutes later, cry at the powerful forgiveness scenes. They eagerly waited for the close-up of her expressive face as she was forgiven or vindicated, and then finally, felt the grand hug with Desi, that was partially obscured by the heart template stretching across the screen with the scrolling credits. Life was magic with Lucy.

Her most powerful legacy was that she gave us laughter, lots of laughter. So what if the chocolate chip cookies burned? Better than the house. Most women rearing families during those years compared themselves with Donna Reed, June Cleaver, and the perfect mother of Timmy in the Lassie family who wore a starched, ironed cotton dress to sling scrambled eggs every morning. And when called to the barn to nurse some dying animal in the dark of night, she wore fashionable low pumps and squatted with her legs together in a ladylike way. What a relief to have Lucy. She gave the American male something to be grateful for—that they weren't married to her.

But I must be honest. That was not the Lucille Ball I knew. Our ten-year friendship occurred during the heady days of my excesses into the world of alcohol and drugs and it was really a matter of convenience for the both of us. We didn't call each other or travel together or really concern ourselves with each other's lives, but we did spend countless hours playing backgammon at the private club, Pips.

Located on Robertson Boulevard in the West Hollywood area, Pips was a private club open only to the rich and famous. It was a popular hangout that had backgammon tables, a disco room, a formal dining area, and a casual dining area. Pips and the other private club, Tramps, which was owned by Jackie Collins and her husband, Oscar, were so private, guests had to be accompanied by members. Most people didn't even know about Tramps at all because it was sequestered away under the Beverly Center.

It was at Pips that I became somewhat friendly with Lucy. Poor thing, at this time in her life, like all of us, she had too much time on her hands. The hairs on the back of my neck would stand up when I heard her screech out my name when I walked into the club. Sometimes I had no tolerance for the unpleasant task of doing something I didn't want to do. Using cocaine and alcohol on a daily basis had shortened my already short fuse.

"Toooooony, Toooooony, Toooooony."

"Lucy, what do you want?" She really got on my nerves.

"Come play backgammon!"

It was so sad to see the icon of comedy bellowing out for anyone to play with her. For the most part, she was alone in her Roxbury home in the flats of Hollywood and she desperately sought out companionship any way she could. Some Sunday nights she would eat out at Matteo's with talk-show host Michael Douglas and his wife, or other friends, but usually she could be found perched at the backgammon tables at Pips looking for someone to keep her company.

I went shopping at Lord and Taylor's one afternoon and saw her Rolls-Royce parked in the parking area at the back of the store. "Oh, shit!" I knew she would try to grab me, and I wanted to avoid her at all costs. Even though I sneaked in, she came up behind me and gripped my neck.

"Toooooony, what are you doing here?"

"I've got to get something, Lucy. I don't have time."

"Yes, you do. Have lunch with me."

"Lucy, I have no time for lunch."

"Yes, you do. You WILL have lunch with me."

So we sat down, had two bottles of champagne, laughed, and ragged, and that was it.

Had my mind not been so chemically altered and revved up, I probably would have been kinder to the fading Hollywood legend, but in my fast-paced world, she was a distraction I didn't want and couldn't tolerate. Now she is frequently a distraction I wholeheartedly embrace as she spins her magic all over again in her television reruns. My mind is clear and can appreciate her genius. Now, I love Lucy.

65

WALLACE

DURING THE 1970S AND 1980S, BRIK JUGGLED FOUR BALLS IN THE air: his dynamic career and three families. Somehow he found time for Wallace and me, and he also continued providing for his first wife and their children. And ours was not an unusual situation in Beverly Hills; in the pursuit of happiness, most of our acquaintances lived an indulgent lifestyle that included cramming every moment with self-satisfying activities.

To be married to a huge star meant compromising one's traditional day-to-day family dream of living in a cozy nest with a mate who actually came home each night. Wallace was not delusional enough to expect that when she married Brik she would have this sort of traditional married life. She had heard the rumors of his infidelities before they wed and she was, after all, very much occupied with her modeling career.

Ours were lives of convenience. I can't speak for Wallace, but I loved the setup; my bills were paid, I was provided for in the grandest sort of way, and I enjoyed the frequent company of my love for 24 years. I assume that she came to the same conclusion and accepted the tradeoff of having social power, money, and public status, all the while sharing its source, who was Brik. Of course, there were occasional awkward encounters between us. We did, after all, inhabit the same fishbowl. One evening Brik and I went to an Italian restaurant in Venice Beach. The beautiful ocean side restaurant was packed that night, but that was no problem for us because we had reservations for our favorite table overlooking the sea. As we swept in, the maître d' quickly approached and cautioned us that Brik's wife was dining with Miss Dinah Shore at a nearby table. I nearly shit because, even though Wallace knew about our relationship, we never flaunted it in front of her or the public. My feet nervously twisted about while we contemplated our dilemma.

As we turned to escape, Wallace saw us and waved with a commanding "I see you; you might as well join us" two-handed motion. Her jewelry flashed in the candlelight. I felt like a dog caught trying to steal a turkey leg off a plate. We approached their table with our tails between our Armani-clad legs. I had always liked Wallace, but the awkwardness of the situation made our initial conversation stilted.

When the waiter came around and asked if he could bring drinks, we all screamed out, "Yes!" We felt like that famous Bette Davis' line in All About Eve: "Buckle your seatbelts, we're in for a bumpy night." Our orders tumbled out in frantic unison—"Harvey Wallbangers, a double shot of tequila, and martinis."

As the night progressed, we became hysterical. Several times Wallace and I dropped our napkins and visited briefly under the table.

"Was he with you Saturday night?"

"No. Wasn't he with you?" I replied, bumping my head under the table.

"NO!"

"Think there could be third woman?"

"No, he couldn't afford it, but more power to him if there is." We burst out in whispered laughter.

The evening passed, and Wallace and I enjoyed each other's company so much we decided to have lunch together sometime in the future. Brik, however, didn't think that was a good idea, so our first encounter was our last. After that, whenever Wallace and I passed each other driving around Beverly Hills or even walking down the street, we would smile, wave, and move on. Our relationship with Brik provided us with what we needed and wanted during those years, but eventually Wallace left Brik for her best friend. No big surprise there. After all, this was Hollywood!

66

MAE

I WAS FORTUNATE ENOUGH TO MEET MAE WEST. ONE SUNDAY morning I was invited to join Irving Rapper and Mae West for a brunch extravaganza known as dim sum. The Warner Brothers director, Irving Rapper, frequently took the aging star to Chinatown for brunch, and I was more than happy to join them that morning.

I waited for their arrival outside the restaurant located in the heart of Chinatown where, surrounded by the surreal backdrop of layered colors, lights, people, smells, and sounds, I observed the swirl of humanity as it went about its day-to-day routine.

Having arrived a few minutes early, I began thinking about Irving Rapper. It had been two months since I'd seen my old friend, and even though he was close to 80 years of age (separating us in age by a good 50 years), we totally enjoyed each other's company. At that time in my life I wasn't fazed or overly impressed with his directorial credits which included: The Glass Menagerie, Rhapsody in Blue, The Corn is Green, Deception, and Now, Voyager. Our friendship was based on the present and filled with laughter and genuine affection for one another. As I waited for them, I smiled remembering my favorite Irving Rapper story.

Irving had told me a great Glass Menagerie story about Tallulah Bankhead's futile attempt to capture the starring role of Amanda Wingfield in the film. During the months preceding the shooting of The Glass Menagerie, Irving waded through endless lists of auditioning actors, script changes, location, and filming decisions. He had made several final decisions concerning a few of the characters but was having trouble with the starring role of the mother in the film. I believe he said Tallulah Bankhead insisted she be tested for the part and the studio pressured him into flying to New York to audition her for the role. On the flight to New York Irving laughed as he told the film crew this story he had heard about her.

Tallulah once attended a midnight mass on Christmas. She had been drinking heavily, and as the priest led the procession with the smoking censer, she loudly proclaimed, "Darling, your gown is lovely, but I'm afraid I have to tell you your purse is on fire."

Knowing that she swilled Old Grand-Dad liquor constantly, and, against his better judgment, Irving gathered a film crew and traipsed up to Tallulah's Algonquin Hotel suite. The screen test was simply a formality to satisfy people who controlled the purse strings at the studio. This maddening waste of time ate at him as they rode the elevator to Miss Bankhead's apartment.

Tallulah had returned to the States after establishing herself on the stage in England. She had enjoyed some success in several films and Broadway shows in the United States, but everyone knew that with the sultry-eyed beauty came a ton of baggage. Her heavy use of alcohol and drugs made a director's job even more difficult; she was not an easy person with whom to work. Irving Rapper could scale a steep directorial mountain;

after all, he had directed Bette Davis and lived to tell about it. But he resented being forced to screen test the tempestuous Bankhead.

Her door opened, "Dahling! How marvelous!"

"Hello, Tallulah."

"Do come in, my dear. So sorry I'm running a bit late. Help yourselves to some tea or bourbon on the table. Go ahead and set up. I'll be right down." She disappeared upstairs.

Irving had the film crew set up the camera, microphone, and lights for the screen test. A fresh canister of film was labeled and placed into the camera; lights were raised and aimed at a divan where Tallulah would read for the role. Just as the last equipment was readied, they heard a stirring at the top of the stairs.

"Dahling!"

Irving and his crew craned their heads to the second story landing where Miss Bankhead stood totally naked except for high heels and a flamboyant hat. She placed her hand on her hip and swivelled to the banister where she pirouetted, affording us a complete view. Her bare arms reached out toward an imaginary audience, her hat tilted up to catch the spotlight that wasn't there: "Now that I have your attention, I'll be right down."

Irving told me that hers was a flawless screen test. What they filmed that day has never been duplicated in the history of Hollywood. It was total perfection. Irving Rapper and his crew left the hotel with performance excellence in the canister, but on arriving back in California, they quickly burned it. He called it, "The world's greatest perfomance that was never seen." He confided that the gifted actress was too unpredictable to risk for the part.

My daydreaming ended when out of the comic book background slid a rather aged black limousine bearing Mae West and Irving Rapper. It dived for the curb and I stood back as the doors opened. My first thoughts were, "My God, she still keeps her image."

Encased in a red well-worn beaded gown complete with kick train and feathers, she unwound herself and gathered up her companion, a Maltese dog who remained paralyzed under her protective arm. Her elbow-length black lace gloves grasped him like he was a Smithsonian treasure. I think I saw him blink, but I never saw him move.

Two handsome bodyguards extended muscular arms toward her and she maneuvered her exit. It was like being there as a time capsule was revealed 50 years down the road. Irving followed and gave me a pat on the back as we entered the restaurant.

We were seated in an authentic Chinese restaurant that was generally frequented by "locals." The other diners hardly looked up as Mae swished by, but they had to have seen her or heard her entrance as the beaded dress rustled and the feather boas stirred the pungent air. After being seated, Mae handed her fluffy companion to the bodyguards and they were dismissed with a backward wave of her hand.

"She lets her eyes do the talking," I thought as I observed her from across the booth. I squinted briefly, and she blurred momentarily into the background concentration of Chinese art and celebration complete with ornately carved wood and detailed paintings. Arched over her was a scaly red dragon that seemed no more unreal than Mae West herself.

That morning she staged a comeback. My God, she had to have been 80, yet she flirted, dramatically poised her lacy arms in the air, and enthralled me with her famous sexual innuendoes. I don't remember her eating a bite.

With an affectedly sexy voice, she said, "Hmmm...Irving darling, should I shock the young lad?"

"Go ahead, Mae. I'm sure I couldn't stop you if I tried. Besides, I'm sure Tony has heard more than you think."

She prepared for the scene by zeroing in on my eyes, and slowly winked at me. Mae West definitely had my attention when she turned her beaded legs out from under the table. I knew I was in for a classic.

She languished for a moment, then with her left hand she sensuously rubbed her left knee.

"Hmmm...this here's Christmas." She coyly smiled at me, lifted her right hand, and rubbed her right knee. "And, hmmm...this here's New Year's." She paused, batted her false eyelashes at me, tipped her feathery hat, and said, "Why don't you come up and see me between the holidaysssss?" I roared with appreciation.

No thanks, Mae, I thought, but just the same, what a thrill to be in her company and to glimpse someone who got away with the outrageous and was admired for it. During the meal, I kept reminding myself that I was viewing the end of an era of Hollywood glamour, and I wished I'd been around earlier to see her in her prime. The waitress delivered the check and three fortune cookies. Mine read, "You will meet many fascinating people during your life."

And I thought, I just did.

67

GARBO

IN CONTRAST TO MAE WEST'S ABILITY TO CONTINUE HER LEGEND long after she needed to, Greta Garbo slipped anonymously away into the pulsating crowds of New York City. It was as if she was just another piece of a puzzle thrown into a huge box with three million others.

When we first got our apartment on Sutton Place and 56th Avenue, I knew that Garbo lived around there, and I became obsessed to see her. It became my goal to spot her some day out walking the streets of New York. I had heard she walked everywhere, and so I vigilantly looked for her at every opportunity. In the storefront windows where crowds paused to do a little shopping, I would briefly view the displays but found myself watching the reflection in the glass to see if I might be missing a Garbo sighting.

Visitors from small towns often think that New Yorkers are heartless, uncaring people. The distant stare in the faces of city dwellers is misconstrued as some coldhearted curse, and yes, it would be in the visitor's small-town environment where people share intimate details of their lives, like menopausal complications, in the grocery line. Eye contact and a slight smile is a requirement in a less-populated town, but in cities like New York, people would be worn out just trying that for one block—hence the dead, deep-in-thought look so commonly seen in NYC.

But not me. I was determined to see Garbo, and that required that I stay on constant alert. I was like a small boy straining to spot Santa and his speeding sleigh in the black December night sky.

Not long after we got the apartment, a friend, Sandra, and I were walking down First Avenue when a woman in a pulled-down knit hat passed us at a quick pace. Breathless, I said to Sandra, "You know what? That was Garbo!"

"You're nuts."

"It was, I swear!" My head twirled around and I memorized her back. Yep, had to be Garbo, I thought.

During the years we lived on Sutton, I thought I saw her several times, but I couldn't be 100 percent sure. I knew she would be alone and nondescript, just a newspaper-wrapped package under the tree. Nothing to rip open first. Nevertheless, I yearned to see her for certain just once before we moved to the Mayfair Regent on Park and 65th.

I was pretty sure I had spotted her from afar several times, but they weren't confirmed sightings. I knew from others that her fast-paced walk was a protection for Garbo. She wasn't out on the streets to mingle with the fascinated starstruck masses. Everyone knew that she didn't want her privacy infringed upon and that she didn't want people yelling out or coming up to her. Her demeanor told passersby that. She didn't trip people with a trailing pink boa trying to get attention as she walked about the city like other old stars might have done.

On one of my last days at the apartment before making our move to the Mayfair Regent, I saw her approaching me on the street. I slowed as the gap between us lessened and shifted to manual focus as I really zeroed in on her. She had to know that I knew who she was. I was short of breath, but respectfully unobtrusive. For several seconds time was suspended; my searching was over; my vigilance rewarded. I positioned myself to pass her and as she brushed by, our eyes locked onto one another's like magnets. Her eyebrows lifted slightly, her eyes twinkled, and she gave me a gift I'll never be able to describe to anyone, a small knowing smile that said to me, "Yes, I'm Garbo." My hunt was over.   Garbo.

68

FRANK

As much as I hated surprise birthday parties, I have to admit that my 35th birthday included something very unique. How many people can claim that Frank Sinatra sang "Happy Birthday" to them? Not many hands out there, I see.

That night in July, we had high expectations as we arrived at Chasen's Restaurant on the outskirts of Beverly Hills. An evening at Chasen's could be counted on to be a delightful indulgence of all the senses. There was tasteful music, rich colors, well-appointed furnishings, and exquisite cuisine; but best of all, it was very private.

Tourists either didn't know about it or couldn't get in or couldn't afford it if they did get in. Chasen's was known for many dishes, but over the years many people came for their chili. It was reported that Elizabeth Taylor had Chasen's chili delivered to her wherever she went.

One could enjoy any of the three separate dining rooms known for their unique personalities. My favorite area had private, hide-away booths richly upholstered with soft burgundy Italian leather.

The surprise birthday party was given by my New York friends who had flown in to help me celebrate my big day, and we were joined by the Beverly Hills contingent. The evening was one of robust toasts and endless funny stories that we relished telling. There was nothing demure or discreet about our parties. No quiet, deep conversations for us. Laughter pealed through the fragrant Chasen's atmosphere as each of us contributed some embarrassing moment or unfortunate incident to the delight of the others. I always felt sorry for people around us. They simply couldn't have been having as much fun as we were.

On my birthday night, however, an elegant party was underway in the adjacent room. The glamorously dressed group included many well-known faces. I spotted Princess Stephanie of Monaco among them. Apparently Gregory Peck was being honored by Frank Sinatra and his friends. Perhaps it was his birthday, too.

Each party raged on well into the night, and when we finally exhausted our appetites and repertoires, the waiter was given the sign for the birthday cake to be delivered to me. Apparently, Frank noticed our festivities, too, and felt generous that evening because that's the only explanation for what happened next.

As the waiter approached my table bearing a beautiful cake in outstretched hands, a booming and familiar voice began singing "Happy Birthday." I turned toward the voice and saw Frank Sinatra standing in the doorway. He raised a crystal glass high, finished the personalized birthday tribute to me, and turned to rejoin his party. We applauded softly and felt strangely warmed by the American icon's thoughtfulness. The "Chairman of the Board" had brought to conclusion a party I'll never forget.

69

J. C.

UNTIL MY MID-30'S I COULD HAVE HAD FRANK SINATRA'S SIGNATURE song, "I Did it My Way" as my theme song. But, with the years came increased turmoil caused by Brik's celebrity, back-stabbing house servants, and my clearer view of what I wanted for myself out of life. When I really thought about it, I realized that we weren't content. My friends and I had only attainable expectations in our day-to-day lives—from food to wheels. It was actually boring in the end. We could have virtually anything we wanted, yet no one was happy. What a paradox...miserable in paradise.

I took stock of my favorite things and found that none of them were possessions. They included, instead, my family, friends, and religion. From my earliest years I felt strongly influenced by The Church and it's teachings and I began to feel increasingly miserable with the self-centered lives I watched spinning out of control all around me. Was I losing my own soul as well? One day at the grocery store, I had a flashback to a story I first heard as a child.

Everyone has probably heard the story of the rich industrialist, Mr. Smith, who was frequently seen sharing his money with the less fortunate. However the story is told, it is emphasized that on countless occasions he reached into his pocket and handed dollars and change to those who lifted a hand in need.

On one fateful evening as Mr. Smith hurriedly left a hotel, he was approached by a beggar who asked for some change. "Not now, Bud. I'm in a terrible rush. Come back tomorrow and I'll take care of you." He ducked into his limousine and was whisked away.

Years later Mr. Smith died and went to the Heavenly Gates, where he was met by Jesus. The Lord reviewed the entries in *The Book* of Mr. Smith's life and declared that there was some good news. "Mr. Smith, you have been extremely generous to others during your time on earth. I like the way you shared your wealth with the less fortunate and the kind deeds you performed." Mr. Smith beamed. "But there is a problem."

"What! I tried to always follow your teachings and take care of the poor. Lord, what do you mean, 'There's a problem'?"

Jesus gently raised his arm to silence Mr. Smith. "Mr. Smith, do you remember the homeless beggar who came to you in need one evening when you were too busy even to reach into your pocket and hand him a dollar?"

"Yes. I told him to return the next day, but I never saw him again."

"Sometimes, Mr. Smith, you only get one chance to prove your worth. That beggar was me."

I cannot begin to describe how much impact that little story had on my life. Was it my Catholic upbringing or parental influence or just an innate sensitive nature? I don't know, but even during my indulgent Beverly Hills days when I was living the fantasy life, I sincerely cared about others and always remembered the Mr. Smith story.

In my own way, I always reached out to others and had varying degrees of success in giving them a helping hand. Some of my intentions, even though good, were misguided to say the least. Once, on the house servant's birthday, I took him out on the town to the tune of about 500 bucks. Sammy seemed to enjoy being treated and indulged, but on our ride home he confided, "Mr. Tony, I want you to know I really appreciate what you did for me this evening, but I hope you don't mind me saying I could have just used the money instead."

What was I thinking? Of course, he would have rather had the $500. I wasn't putting myself in his shoes. That was the Beverly Hills versus Reality conflict that surfaced constantly.

One day I found myself standing in the grocery line at Ralph's in Century City. I was mildly annoyed that there were three people in front of me, and I glanced into the cart to see if I really wanted the items. Was it really worth the wait? Not much was in my basket, just some last-minute delicacies for some impromptu guests, but I decided I'd suffer through.

My fingers were drumming out a tune on the buggy handle and at first I was mildly amused by the hubbub of the cashiers, baggers, and frantic women digging into their overloaded purses trying to unearth a wallet or checkbook. Very quickly, however, my patience waned. The line hadn't moved at all since I had joined it. I leaned over the two customers in front of me who had already laid out their purchases onto the motionless conveyor belt and had grabbed tabloids to paralyze their minds from the delay we were experiencing.

That's when I tuned into a conversation at the front of the line. The cashier was saying, "Ma'am, you need more money." Blah, blah, blah. I couldn't hear it all. I maneuvered a bit until I saw the problem. A tiny, bent woman had her worn handbag clutched in both hands against her chest and was utterly distraught. Whimpering sounds came from her pale lips, and she appeared to be confused about whether she should scurry out without her few canned goods or wait and suffer more indignities. The poor embarrassed woman tugged on her gold wedding band and offered it to the cashier for collateral. The cashier shook her head and announced the store policy one more time. It was clear that whatever the problem, they were putting her through hell and that she couldn't understand the dilemma.

I caught the manager's eye and waved to him. "What's the problem?" I asked.

"The old bat doesn't have enough money. She can't speak English very well."

"Well, let her go, for God's sake. I'll take care of it. Don't embarrass her any further. Tell her it was a mistake."

"Yes, sir."

The manager whispered into the cashier's ear and, just like an opened floodgate, the line began to move. With a clatter and a squeak of the handcart, the old lady gathered her groceries and scuttled away into the bright California day. When I reached the cashier, I asked her the amount of the lady's purchase.

"$11.61, sir," the cashier replied.

"What? Are you kidding? You mean that poor old lady was held hostage for $11.61? Here." I paid the cashier and hurried out to catch a glimpse of her, but just like a ghost she had disappeared.

I replayed the scene in my mind, remembered the Mr. Smith story, and winked to the sky. "Not this time, J.C.!"

70

VON

EVERYONE LEARNS TO HANDLE CONFLICTS FROM OBSERVING THEIR own family's interactions. In my family we confronted problems and vocalized our concerns to each other without fear of severing our ties as a close-knit unit. A concerned criticism aimed at a sibling or a parent was not presented as an attack or an unkind cut, just a reflection of one's perception that things were getting out of hand. My loving and caring parents raised the three of us in a warm, family-oriented home.

For instance, when I was doing poorly in school and was on the verge of being unmanageable, there was a family meeting and the problem was discussed. As we sat around the dining room table, my obnoxious behavior was presented in almost scientific terms, "unable to meet educational expectations," "some willful disregard for authority," etc. I could see a real concern on my parent's faces for my well being and future and had to admit that I really had screwed up and needed more structure in my life. I learned to confront problems, take action, and accept the consequences of my decisions.

Our opinions were expected and valued, even as children, and we weren't punished for having divergent ideas about things, if they were thought out and supported with some kind of reasoning. I remember a nightly ritual at my house where Mom would completely dress into some chosen outfit for the next day. We were called upon to give our opinions of her appearance. Sometimes we suggested another blouse, accessory, or shoe. And even though we realized this ritual was all about Mom's obsessions and ego, we learned that our opinions mattered and were valued.

As an adult, I embraced friends with a real concern for their welfare and happiness. There was no doubt that I enjoyed indulging myself with fine foods, clothes, cars, and frequent travel, but I found myself deeply concerned, some would say obsessed, with my friends' problems. Not all of my interactions and intentions with friends became positive ones; some were wasted, pissed into the wind. I have some regrets.

In the late 1970s I met by chance one of my favorite people, Von. I was in the New York Academy of Performing Arts with Bette when Von was introduced to us through mutual friends. His quick wit and insatiable desire to laugh and enjoy life were infectious. We perfectly complemented each other and were as close as two people could be. Ours was not a sexual relationship, however. In some ways I felt that we were even closer than that.

Von and I were in sync with one another. We had similar tastes in humor and similar outlooks on the world. Compare us to salt and pepper. We even resembled these complementary ingredients because I was the dark, tangy, shocking one and Von was Scandinavian blond, slightly chunky, and had a strong personality that definitely seasoned any social gathering. He was interesting; he was the salt. Without Von, life could be dull.

For one thing, he spoke seven languages fluently and had traveled to every continent. He didn't drink life in; he gulped it down. With the help of drugs and booze, he was fueled for his constant pursuit of the good life, and that included a promiscuous sex life. He would return from some disastrous dalliance with some guy he'd met and have me in stitches for hours as he reenacted a comedy of errors. Once he fell off a balcony giving some guy a blow job. I dearly loved him.

While I was in Beverly Hills, Von moved in with me for a six-month stay. I introduced him to my circles of friends, and he was quickly accepted as a fun-loving addition to all but the most exclusive occasions. Having a houseguest was, for the most part, very enjoyable. I shared my clothes with him, bought him outfits when I shopped for myself, and made sure he had extra money to pay for friends' meals at the finest restaurants. Eventually Von got an apartment and a job in the travel business. We made many trips together over the next ten years and deeply enjoyed each other's company.

Gradually, however, drugs and alcohol began chiseling away at our lives. He began taking risks of enormous proportions. His risks weren't limited to misguided sexual escapades; his choice of companions greatly endangered his safety many times. Toward the late 1980s, I withdrew from cocaine and alcohol and became so dissatisfied with my life that I began my plan for escape. Not exactly Escape from Alcatraz, but an escape from a mindless loop of parties, extravagant living, fragile relationships, and wasted lives.

The unrest that prompted my decision to clean up my act was based on the glaring evidence that the drug-and-alcohol lifestyle was a damning existence in the end and that spending my whole life being fucked up was not worth it. To my knowledge Von never came to that conclusion.

As I slowly formulated a plan for escape, I became determined that he seek help for his drug and alcohol addiction.

My concern for him grew; I offered to send him to the Betty Ford Clinic, but he loudly denied having a drug or alcohol problem. How could he not see that he was in need of help? I so desperately wanted to help him, but that desire drove a wedge into our relationship. We had been in such accord, but then we each stubbornly crossed our arms and stared across the chasm that separated us.

I last saw Von at a party at my house. The theme was "Simply Heavenly," and I had the staircase entwined with gold-and-white ribbons and angels and clouds. It truly looked like the stairway to Heaven with each step lighting up in succession to the second story landing. The house was stunningly decorated, but I can't think about it without remembering it as one of the worst moments of my life.

I happened upon Von pulling out some dollar bills from the tip drawer in the kitchen. The money was for tipping service people who delivered things at the service entrance of the house. Another guest, not wanting to be suspected for the theft, reported that he had also seen Von tuck away some liquor into his duffle bag earlier in the afternoon.

It would have been easy to ignore his bad behavior if I had been raised in a different way, but it was my nature to confront problems and air them out, not look the other way. So, before he slipped away that evening, I told him I had seen him take the money. I did not ask for it back or further demean him by asking him to open his duffle bag, but I informed him that he would not be welcome back into my house until he sought help for his addiction problem. Again, I offered my financial help, but it was firmly rejected. And that was the last I saw of my dear friend Von. He walked out of my life, but not out of my heart.

I knew that my advice to him was correct and that he was jeopardizing his life by refusing help, but the issues at stake collapsed the bridge between us. I was as unreachable to him as he was unreachable to me. For some time he left messages on my answering machine and sent a few cards, but eventually I heard no more from him. I had taken my stand.

Several years passed and then I heard that my dear, lost friend had died of AIDS. I was devastated by the news. There was no way to get to his funeral, but I wrote him a letter of closure and burned it in a ceremony at the base of a double weeping cherry tree I planted in his name.

Did he know he had the disease when I saw him last? If so, why should he have wanted help? Why should he have changed then? Even though I was right in wanting to help Von, I live with my decisions from that night and regret being robbed of years with one of my closest friends. I regret trying to force him to accept decisions that were mine, not his.

71

DESTRUCTION

PRESSURES MOUNTED AS THE SERVANTS BECAME MORE INTRUSIVE in my life. Instead of lightening my load, they weighed me down with extra, unexpected problems. Not a week went by that I wasn't approached for money or emotional support from one of the servants or their families. Sometimes the North Beverly house seemed like a gilded trap, and I was the schmuck who had his ass caught in it.

To outsiders, it probably seemed like a fairy-tale existence, but as the years slid by, I gradually began to resent the envy of the servants. I rambled around in the beautiful rooms and felt limited pleasures. Never far from my mind was the rag of the day. With the exception of Hattie, each servant brought his or her own version of misery into my life. In many ways I haplessly played into their greedy little hands because I was afraid they would terminate their job and go to the tabloids. Sometimes, I had the nerve to refuse them their requests, and then hours later I would hear a sulking voice mumbling, "*National Enquirer* sure would be interested in talking to me."

These rumblings, along with continued years of drugs and alcohol and the demise of many of my friend's marriages, began to take their toll on me. During our years together, Brik had seen unique temper tantrums from me. From the "big move" and shredding his clothes out of the penthouse window to the floating duck and ruined dinner evening, I certainly had created memorable emotional outbursts throughout the years.

My dissatisfactions with being out of control in my day-to-day life reached a new crescendo one April day as I prepared to have lunch with Jan Myles. We had planned to meet at Cravings. As I completed dressing, I told Sammy, "Put the top down on the Mercedes. I'll take it."

I slid into the beautiful black-and-grey Mercedes, put the key into the ignition, and found the fucking thing was dead. My hands hit the steering wheel as I threw the keys into the back seat and flung myself out of the car. "Sammy! Bring me the keys to the Rolls." And he did.

After I turned the key in the Rolls-Royce and found that it too was dead, I became so enraged, my heart almost began fibrillating. Sammy was paid to keep the cars running. It was his meager responsibility to have them in good working order. That was his job, and once again, I was screwed by his negligence. Besides, I had heard that when I was away, he went around town saying he was Tony and that the Rolls was his. I was furious over that.

"I don't want to be chauffeur-driven to Sunset Plaza," I growled at his suggestion. "This all eats shit!"

Sammy slipped away as I felt myself heat up to a rolling boil. "All of these fucking cars, and not one even works!"

I charged back to the Mercedes, released the emergency brake, and watched it begin its slow backward descent down the driveway. Next in line for the demolition was the Rolls.

With a quick snap, I released its emergency brake and helped the heavy mother along with a strong push of my foot.

The destruction was slow to materialize. It took a while for the two cars to build up backward speed. However, just as I reached the limousine and let off its emergency brake, there was a satisfying crash. It took more effort to get the limo moving, but it was well worth it because it really created an amazing sight careening wildly down the steep driveway right toward the other two mangled luxury cars. With a quick, satisfying glance, I could see the three cars clumped together at the foot of the hill near the entrance gate; a silent tribute to my fury.

This was by no means the end of my rage. I grabbed the phone and called Brik, who was out on the golf course. Some guy at the clubhouse answered my call and evidently realized that I was going to speak to Brik, even if he was on the thirteenth hole. This was before cellular phones, so someone actually had to go find him and bring him back for the unnerving news that I was flipping out and felt justified in doing so. This is some of what Brik heard when he angrily answered the phone.

"I didn't want all of these fucking $100,000 cars! All I wanted was something reliable. I just wanted a LeBaron. Get me the fuck out of here." I started going crazy.

He said, and rightly so, "If that's what you want, go get it."

My mind was racing as I mentally looped through the car tensions. There was never one time when all three cars were working. The problems with them were continuous, and everything costs so much in Beverly Hills. Every time a car went in for repairs the bill was never less than $1,000. Between the car situation and the people who had their hands out at every turn, things really began to eat away at me. Add the drugs and booze, and I believe my emotional stability was depleted.

As I was leaving that afternoon, I said, "Sammy, just call me a fucking cab, and let me get out of here."

"Tony, what do you want me to do with those cars?"

"As far as I'm concerned, go get a gallon of gasoline and burn the shit out of all of them."

The servants were scared that day and figured that I'd come home and kill them all. Instead, the gathering clouds of dissatisfaction continued to collect in my mind and I began entertaining thoughts of moving. It just didn't seem worth it anymore.

72

IT'S OVER!

THE YEARS PASSED QUICKLY...YEARS OF EXTREME PRIVILEGE AND—
toward the end—months of feeling captive. I was the cherished
object of people's fascination. From my self-imposed position
in the golden arena, I endlessly preened and performed. With
an obsessive fervor, I interacted in the lives of my friends and
family and held myself to the highest physical and social
standards. Hey, this was hard work.

The paradox continued: I dearly loved and deeply despised
life in the gilded cage. I began to anguish at the oppressive
paparazzi-curiosity our suspected relationship created, problems
with the household help, and the hopelessness I saw all about
me.

In reality, I knew no one enjoyed more freedom than I did.
I had the means to go wherever I wanted, buy anything that
appealed to me, and set the pace of my life to suit myself, but
I began to long for a simpler, more meaningful life. I felt God's
gentle whisper in my ear. Remember Peggy Lee's song "Is that
all there is, my friend?"

One summer evening, like countless ones before, I readied
myself for a formal affair, "The Rock Hudson AIDS Benefit."

To complement my favorite Versace tuxedo, I chose beautiful one-carat diamond studs. Full-length mirrors reflected perfection—a deep tan, a toned body, and self-confidence. I glanced down at the elegant invitation and didn't even bother to smile. How many of these things had I been to over the years?

My driver delivered me to the Beverly Hilton Grand Ballroom where doormen met me with the usual exaggerated friendliness. I pressed through the glittering crowd to find my table for the evening of entertainment and thinly disguised financial appeals. Elizabeth Taylor, Malcomb Forbes, Francesca Hilton, Merv Griffin, and Eva Gabor were seated at my table. Of course, Brik arrived a bit late.

Perched between enormous leafy plants and formally set tables (proudly decked out with the white-and-gold theme) were television cameras ready to capture all the excitement and glamour that night. It was being taped to be aired on cable TV at a later date. Every sip of champagne, every jewel's sparkle, and even the flirtatious exchanges between hopeful lovers were captured for the millions of everyday people who would have just died to be there. The night was filled with marvelous entertainment, the finest music, drinks, and endless trays of beautifully prepared foods. This crowd expected the best.

Our table-mates exchanged conversations and gossipy observations with us, but these only mildly captured my interest. I told a few of my stories only to realize that I was losing interest in pleasing an audience. I doubt if they noticed because during the course of the evening and after numerous drinks, attentions wandered and people began saying what was really on their minds—it sure sounded like bitching to me.

Acquaintances dropped by our table and shared more than I ever wanted to know about themselves. Eventually I tuned out the troubled babble of people's disappointing lives and let my mind wander. Occasionally snippets of their conversations registered in my mind. Could it be that they were only consumed with the trouble in their lives? Were they unable to reflect on the grandness of life, the cherished miracle of it all? To me, it sounded like they endured a miserable existence, certainly not the lifestyle the adoring public believed they had.

The dream-like state I was in allowed me to listen objectively to the comments I heard and to categorize them into piles of dissatisfactions consisting of: children or spouses on drugs and alcohol, exorbitant costs at rehabilitation clinics, servant ungratefulness, their under-appreciated talents, and the high costs of plastic surgery. My God, I thought, is no one happy? Am I happy? I would never have Brik totally to myself and for some reason that mattered to me now. Life seemed so short. Would it be spent alone?

Such a simple truth had been hidden from me for so many years. Anyone watching the televised show of this event would assume that these privileged people were consumed with happiness. Still in a conversational fog, yet enjoying 20/20 clarity, I began to plan my escape from my increasingly disappointing Beverly Hills' life. Yes, it was time to go.

After the benefit was over, Sammy brought me home to an empty house. Painful thoughts encircled me and constricted my breathing—an empty house, an empty heart. With a consuming sadness, I climbed the stairs to my suite, and with each step my divided and confused heart confirmed my growing decision to leave Beverly Hills.

On the landing at the top of the dark stairs, I collapsed into an exhausted heap. The reality of missing the importance of life overpowered me. A flood of tears broke from me as I slowly pulled off my tie and unbuttoned my shirt. There in the luxurious darkness I cried unending tears. I had finally realized the frightening truth—that it was time to leave, and to leave for good.

As the fear and emotion of making such a monumental decision subsided, I felt strangely empowered, determined, and sure of the correctness of my plan. I should say our plan because I had prayed to God for guidance and a larger purpose in my life. His persistent whispers had opened the door to my gilded cage and I flew away without a backward glance.

73

Ring

ERIC FINGERED THE FEW REMAINING PAGES AND SLOWLY CLOSED the manuscript. The hours had flown by and it was time to drive home.

Traffic was heavy during Eric's ride home. Nothing unusual about that. Today, however, he didn't mind because the extra time gave him an opportunity to think about the new manuscript. He could hardly wait to finish it and had decided to give a favorable note of intent to the writer who was, ironically, a Georgian.

As the traffic inched along, he began mentally editing some of the episodes. He thought: Some bridging is needed to smooth the story transitions. His childhood stories seem a bit forced, but we can work on that later. Perhaps we could leave out a marriage or two. No, they are so funny. Everyone can identify with wedding fiascoes. The Beverly Hills stories can't really be true, can they? Some names will have to be changed, just in case. At any rate, true or not, it is some roller coaster ride that has "New York Times Best Seller list" written all over it.

He finally pulled onto Oakwood Drive and was relieved to see no news crews gathered in his yard. That dream seemed so long ago. He gathered up his coffee cup and briefcase and walked past the trickling fountain near the trellis. His arrival was heralded by incessant barks from Cody and Cali. He laughed out loud as he watched them through the kitchen window as they became airborne demonstrating their highest trampoline leaps for him.

Matthew prepared marinated chicken on the grill and they picnicked outside that evening. They reviewed the day and indulged themselves in several strolls around the yard to admire the new flowers and foliage. This was their favorite time of day, just the two of them and their "boys" following every step and smelling every flower.

Some neighbors came over for a while and temporarily broke the spell, but soon the day was gone and night visited the tired couple. Throughout the evening Eric hadn't mentioned the manuscript, but he was hardly able to contain his interest in the final pages of the book.

At last, everyone had settled in. Matthew had turned away from the light and had fallen into a deep sleep with Cali curled at his feet. Eric quietly opened the cardboard box and pulled out the last sheets and began reading.

That was it. I decided to leave California forever. I simply could not live here another minute. As hard as it was going to be to leave Brik, the financial luxuries, the social status, good friends, and all I had known for the past 24 years, I decided to begin a new life.

Brik believed I'd change my mind, but with the simple purchase of an airline ticket, I boarded flight 479 for New Jersey. As the plane waited to taxi down the runway at LAX, I nestled my head into the fresh pillow, smiled vacantly at the well-dressed traveler seated next to me, and raised a finger to the stewardess. "Yes, I'd like a glass of champagne, please...Thank you."

I held the glass up and stared into the ascending bubbles: "Here's to the good life, and here's to the new life, good or bad." I lifted the champagne and took a small sip.

Why was I leaving the money, drama, privilege, and excitement? For some time I had been aware of moral stirrings and dissatisfactions in my life. I had never really wanted house servants or a Rolls-Royce or the nightly parade—dressed up and dining with others who found themselves at a dead end facing overwhelming anxieties about their drug-and-alcohol-dependent children, other personal dissatisfactions, and living with the despondency of not knowing what else to wish for. The plane taxied down the runway, gathering speed, and as its nose lifted off, I toasted the City of Angels dropping away beneath me.

Yes, I was on my own, but now every decision and accomplishment would be mine as I put my life into God's hands to direct me toward my destiny. The plane pulled to the right and I peered out of the window toward the exquisite red sunset over the Pacific Ocean. I would miss the ocean and certain household furnishings, but I had taken my silver, furs, and jewelry with me. The plane gained altitude and flew toward a double rainbow. That was a good sign, I thought. Suddenly, a shaft of sunlight cut through the oval window and ignited the emerald-and-gold Bulgari ring I always wore on my left hand. Once again I raised a toast, "Here's to Beverly Hills."

The End.

Air rushed into Eric's lungs as he lowered the manuscript. "My God," he gasped looking with new eyes at his sleeping companion. He could barely whisper Matthew's name as his trembling hand reached for the light switch. His emerald-and-gold ring flashed goodnight and Matthew smiled into his pillow.

Thank you, Margie

To order copies of *Both Sides of the Rainbow* please contact Arcangela Press, Inc. Suite 240 #A, 3605 Sandy Plains Road, Marietta, GA 30066. Books can be ordered on the Internet at http://www.bothsidesoftherainbow.com.